CHASING THE NHL:

From Pond Hockey to Pro
The Trent Daavettila Story

Book design by:
Arbor Services, Inc.
www.arborservices.co/

Printed in the United States of America

Chasing the NHL: From Pond to Pro, The Trent Daavettila Story
Jay Storm

1. Title 2. Author 3. Sports

Library of Congress Control Number: 2017914434
ISBN 13: 978-0-692-95255-9

CHASING THE NHL:

From Pond Hockey to Pro
The Trent Daavettila Story

Jay Storm

Storm Publishing

Contents

Chapter One

"What I'm about to tell you is gonna sound like the craziest thing you've ever heard." Those were the first words I said to Kenny Holland, general manager of the Detroit Red Wings. "But I ain't crazy, and I'm not nuts. All I can tell you is that I'm right."

I had been calling Kenny for nearly two weeks straight, pestering his secretary Kim.

"Who's calling?" she asked.

"This is Jay."

"Jay who?"

"Just tell Kenny, Jay's calling."

"Okay, Jay. In regards to what?"

"Jay called, and he needs to talk to Kenny."

And then I'd hang up the phone.

When Trent Daavettila and I started out, I didn't know the first thing about being a pro sports agent, but I sure as heck knew how to run a business. And I knew that if I had business to do in the world of professional hockey, that business would start with Kenny Holland.

So there I was, working in my insurance agency in the town of Farmington, Michigan, a suburb of Detroit, and I told the people

1

working in my office that if a guy named Kenny Holland called, I didn't care what I was doing or who I was talking to, get me on the phone with him. Kenny didn't realize it yet, but he was lucky I was trying to get in touch with him. Trent Daavettila was an NHL-caliber hockey player, an extreme talent that was going to waste on ponds, backyard rinks, and with the men's league in Houghton, Michigan. Sure, he was smaller than most NHL players, and at that time he didn't train as hard as the other guys at the professional hockey level. But the talent he displayed on the ice was on a far higher level than what I was used to—the passing, the vision, his hockey sense—all completely off the charts. I knew if he put in the work to get stronger and bigger, Trent could play professional hockey, and perhaps even in the NHL when all was said and done.

Chapter Two

Trent had been recognized as an above-average hockey talent since he was about twelve years old—from peewees, bantams, on up through high school—but he hadn't been led down the traditional path that most pros go down—AAA hockey, youth training camps, summer workouts, and all that. His family was a hockey family, but his parents didn't have time to help Trent develop his talent. He had eleven brothers and sisters. Trent was the second oldest, and his parents had more important things to do than run one kid around to hockey events all the time. But still, his talents as a hockey player shown through whatever lack of opportunity he may have experienced. By the time I saw him play in the men's leagues, I knew right away that he had natural gifts on the ice.

Trent grew up near me in Howell, a town in southeast Michigan. He was a good kid, always looking out for his brothers and sisters. With shaggy blond hair and blue eyes, he was never the biggest kid out there on the ice, but he was quick, had a good center of gravity, and could navigate the rink like he had eyes in the back of his head.

Howell, like many small towns in Michigan, is a hockey town, and Trent's dad was a hockey dad. Trent began playing hockey when he was only four years old—that's when his dad built him and his siblings a rink in their backyard.

When the moment finally came and I got Detroit Red Wings general manager Kenny Holland on the phone, Trent was playing in the men's leagues while attending Michigan Tech earning an engineering degree. I had previously called Jamie Russell, the Michigan Tech hockey coach at the time, and told him his team needed to take Trent and red shirt him. They told Trent to try out for the team but cut him nearly immediately, likely only because of his size. I'm sure Russell regrets cutting Trent now.

Trent had been playing organized hockey for about ten years, from the peewees up to the men's leagues. I remember the first time I saw him play, and I said to myself, well gosh darn it if this kid doesn't remind me of Pavel Datsyuk of the Detroit Red Wings. Compared to the rest of the guys out there on the ice, and there were good players in those summer leagues—college players, even NHL players—Trent was obviously one of the best players by far.

So I got to thinking about what a shame it was Trent was talented enough to be playing for the Detroit Red Wings, but nobody else was giving him credit for those talents. At that time I already had an established insurance agency. When I started in the insurance business I used to cold call four to six hours a day. I thought I could transfer those phone skills into getting some pro tryouts lined up for Trent.

When Trent was finishing up his bachelor's degree at Michigan Tech in the spring of 2008, I called him up one day out of the blue and said, "Trent, I know you're a great hockey player—you're good enough to go pro—and I was just wondering if you had any interest in pursuing that path?"

Trent laughed and said, "Well, yeah, I mean, I would love to try it, but how the heck you gonna do that, Jay?"

"I'm not sure yet," I said, "but if I get you a chance to try out somewhere, would you do it?"

"Well, yeah, I'd do it," he said.

"But would you do anything to get a chance to play professional hockey?"

"Anything?"

"Well, yeah, anything. It's going to take a lot of work, that's for sure, and I want to make sure you're 100 percent committed to this. Otherwise, you know, I don't want to waste my time, or your time for that matter."

"Jay, I would do anything for a chance to play pro hockey."

"Listen, Trent, from here on out, I want you to remember one thing—I know you're good enough to play in the NHL, so I am going to do my darnedest to make sure you get a shot doing just that. Now, I know it may seem like a long shot, but the NHL is our end goal, and I'm not going to quit until you get a shot to play at that level. How does that sound?"

"To be honest, the NHL sounds kinda nuts. I mean, I didn't even make the Tech team, Jay. You really think the NHL is our best bet?"

"Believe me, Trent, you belong in the NHL. And I'm not going to stop trying until you get your shot. Let me handle the business end of things; you just be sure to be ready to play when you get the call. Okay?"

"All right, if I get the call to play pro hockey, you can be sure I'll be ready to give it a shot."

"That's what I wanted to hear. I'm going to get started, then. Hold tight, I'll be in touch."

Chapter Three

After hearing the conviction in Trent's voice, I hung up the phone and went to bed satisfied, knowing that when tomorrow came I would have a new project to work on.

When I got in the shower the next morning, I started brainstorming about how to get Trent to the next level—beyond the men's leagues. Now I may have let on that I knew how to be a pro sports agent, but the truth is, I didn't know the first step. I had never worked in the business, and I hadn't read any books about it nor had anybody given me any advice. I was completely alone on this new quest of mine.

My mind was racing. I knew that Trent deserved more, but how to get him what he deserved was beyond me. Sure, I knew I wanted NHL scouts to see what I had seen of Trent's talent, but I couldn't tell what direction to take my first step.

I got out of the shower, patted my face, and looked up at the mirror. I'm about a decade and a half older than Trent, and looking at myself that morning, cleanly shaven and with my sandy-colored hair freshly cut, I was reminded of what I would have wanted if someone had tried to help me get to the pros when I was Trent's age. I looked myself square in the eyes and said, "Jay, if you wanna piss with the big dogs, you'd better start calling them."

I thought, *Who's the biggest big dog I've ever heard of?* And the name that kept coming to mind was Kenny Holland, the general manager of the Detroit Red Wings. He was the man who had brought the Red Army, aka the Russian Five, into Detroit and built the team that would eventually win four Stanley Cups between 1997 and 2008.

I figured since Kenny Holland had the eye to pick guys like Pavel Datsyuk out of the middle of Siberia on his way to making one of the greatest sports franchises in history, then he should be able to recognize Trent's talent, despite the fact that Trent hadn't come from any Division I school and wasn't being touted by some high-profile professional scout.

Chapter Four

How was I, an insurance agent playing men's league hockey in rural Michigan with no sports management experience, supposed to get the attention of one of the most successful NHL general managers of all time?

One thing about me, however, is that I'm extremely persistent. In the insurance business you make a living off making phone calls. I had built my entire business with simply a phone book and a telephone. Now I was determined to use the same logic and determination I had used to start my business and apply it to helping Trent.

I developed a philosophy, as I was finding success in the insurance business, that has gone on to work for me not only in my business ventures but in nearly all my dealings with other people. That philosophy is based around three core elements that I found to be the foundation of what is needed to be successful: enthusiasm, optimism, and persistence. I knew then, when I was starting off on this venture, that if I was going to get Trent the kind of respect he deserved from professional hockey organizations, I would need to tout his playing abilities with enthusiasm, remain optimistic no matter what the obstacle, and never display any fear that we would not reach our goal.

So I picked up the phone and went to work. If I was going to find a way in to pro hockey, it would be by persistently calling Joe Louis Arena and asking for Kenny Holland. So I googled the phone number for Joe Louis Arena.

I called, asked for Kenny Holland, and got transferred to his secretary, Kim. "Hello, Kenny Holland's office, Detroit Red Wings. Kim speaking."

I said, "Hey, Kim, is Kenny around?"

"No, he's not. Can I take a message?"

"Sure. Have him give Jay Storm a call."

"Okay," she said. I gave her my number.

I waited for Kenny's call until the following afternoon. No call yet from Kenny, unsurprisingly, given that I was an NHL nobody calling out of the blue. I decided to call back. Same routine: call Joe Louis Arena, get transferred up to Kenny Holland's office, and Kim would answer the phone.

"It's Jay Storm calling back," I said. "I want to make sure Kenny got the message."

"Oh yeah, Jay, he got the message. Can I ask what this is in regards to?" said Kim.

"Just have him give me a call," and then I'd hang up the phone.

Next day. Still no call. So I'd do the same thing all over again. Kim would say, "Hey, Jay! How you doing?"

"Doing good! You know, Kim, I never heard back from Kenny."

"Yeah, I know, Jay. But what's this in regards to anyway?"

"Well, it's in regards to a hockey player. Have him give me a call."

Each day I'd do this, day after day, every day giving Kim a little more information. After about the thirtieth phone call and two weeks later, I said to Kim, "Listen, I'm gonna keep calling back each and every single day. Hopefully Kenny calls me back, because I'm not gonna quit calling until either you guys stop answering the phone or he calls me back. Now listen, I'll leave messages every single day if I have to, because I know I've got to talk to Kenny about this hockey player." She laughed. Luckily Kim and I got along, and she found a humor in my persistence. She told me that she thought Kenny would call me back.

One day, Samantha, who used to work in my office, hollered back to me, "Jay, Kenny Holland is on the line." I was in the middle of a good sales call, but I hung up and transferred over to the line where Kenny was waiting.

"Hey, Ken, this is Jay Storm. Thanks a million for calling me back."

"Yeah, Jay. Kenny Holland here. I heard you've been trying to get in touch with me about a hockey player."

"Oh, Ken," I said, "let me tell you, I've got something good for you. You're not going to regret talking to me. Do you have five minutes?"

"Yeah, yeah," he said, "I've got five minutes for you."

"What I'm about to tell you may sound like the craziest thing you've ever heard, but you've got to hear me out. I'm not crazy. I'm not nuts. All I can tell you is that I'm right. You see, Ken, there's one thing you and I have in common."

"What's that, Jay?" he asked.

"Well . . . ," I paused for a second, "we both recognize talent."

"Oh, okay," he said, chuckling a bit. "So tell me this first, Jay. Where's your guy playing right now?"

"That's the thing, Kenny. It's a unique situation." I knew Ken was gonna ask me this. "You're gonna think I'm crazy, but I'm not. I'm gonna tell you the truth, he's playing recreational hockey, you know, in the men's leagues."

"He's playing where?"

"Men's league, you know? Pickup hockey?"

"Men's league?"

"Yeah."

"Pickup?"

"That's right."

"You do realize you're speaking to the Detroit Red Wings of the NHL, don't you?"

"I know, I know. I know who you are. But I'm telling you, he's a late bloomer who's been playing in a men's league at Dee Stadium up in Houghton." This got his attention, because Houghton is a huge hockey town—the place where pro hockey was first invented. "Here's a kid that I've been watching since high school. He used to be small and weak when he graduated from high school, and Michigan Tech cut him. But they screwed up. They're the worst team in the WCHA and they have their best player playing shinny on the other side of town. Now he's about to graduate college and he's physically matured—six foot, 180 pounds. I've been watching him play recreational hockey the last couple years, and I'm telling you right now, this guy is a diamond in the rough. He makes the other guys look like they drank too much

Molson and are doggy paddling around in the deep end. I'm calling you because I know you found all those great hockey players over in Russia and drafted them in the late rounds. You understand late bloomers—guys that physically mature later on. You're good at finding talent, and so am I. And I'm telling you, this kid is phenomenal. He's like a young Pavel Datsyuk. If you give him two years, I guarantee you he'll be playing in the NHL, if somebody would just give him a shot. You've got to take a look at him, Ken."

"Well, Jay. He does sound intriguing. I like your enthusiasm and I love your passion," said Holland. "So I'll tell you what. I'm gonna have one of my top two scouts give you a call. That's Jim Nill or Ron Sanko. One of those two guys will give you a call and we'll take a look at this kid."

"Awesome, Ken. When can I expect their call?"

"They'll call you sometime in the next few days."

"Thank you very much, sir," I said and hung up the phone.

Chapter Five

I was on my way home from work that night after talking to Kenny Holland when my phone rang.

"Hi, Jay. It's Ron Sanko. Kenny Holland gave me your number. He tells me you've got a player I need to look at. I'm the top scout for the Detroit Red Wings, and I'm also the general manager of the Flint Generals in the IHL, and I want to take a look at this player."

"Ron," I said, "I'm telling you right now. He's a good kid and a phenomenal hockey player. He just needs someone to give him a shot at the next level."

"Well, let me ask you, Jay. Where's he playing right now, at this moment?"

"He's playing in a men's league tournament over in Wisconsin," I said.

"Can you get him to Flint this weekend?" asked Ron. It was five p.m. on a Thursday night.

"Yes. Where are you playing tomorrow night?"

"Tomorrow we're in Kalamazoo. Saturday and Sunday we're home. Can you have him in Kalamazoo tomorrow night?"

"That'll be tough," I said. "He has a game in Wisconsin tonight."

"Okay. How about Saturday in Flint?"

14

"That's good, Ron. Wait until you see this kid. You're gonna love him."

I hung up the phone and immediately called Trent.

Chapter Six

By the time I got home from work that night, I had tried calling Trent about ten times. I was super frustrated that he wasn't picking up. The way I saw it, if we didn't start moving on any opportunity as soon it became available, Trent would be looked over for the next guy. Being that he was coming out of a men's league instead of a draft or a Division I school, the deck was already stacked against us, so I didn't want to waste a single second when an offer was on the table.

At the time I didn't realize Trent's game in Wisconsin started at seven p.m. So around ten p.m. my phone lit up. Trent was calling.

"Jay, I see I've got ten missed calls from you. What's going on?"

"Trent, remember when I asked you if I could get you a shot playing pro hockey, would you give it everything you've got?"

"Well, of course I remember that."

"Okay, because I got you a shot. You've got to get to Flint for a game Saturday night. You're gonna suit up for the Flint Generals."

"Jay, are you serious?"

"Heck yeah I'm serious."

"How on earth did you make that happen?" asked Trent, sounding slightly incredulous.

"Don't worry about how I made it happen. What's important is that you're ready to go for the Generals on Saturday night. Now remember how I told you that the goal was the NHL? This is the first step. So keep your eye on the prize, and let's make it happen. Are you going to be ready to go in Flint on Saturday night?"

"All right, I can be there—absolutely. I'll leave in the morning."

Chapter Seven

The next morning at eleven a.m. I gave Trent a call again. He sounded bright eyed and bushy tailed, and told me he was on his way to Michigan, just having a smoke.

"A smoke!" I said. "What the heck are you doing smoking? You're about to go play pro hockey! You've got to quit!"

Trent laughed and said, "Ah, jeez, I guess you're right. That'll probably be my last drag off a cigarette."

"Darn right it will be. You're going pro, man! Remember, Trent, keep your eye on the prize. Don't let something stupid like a darn cigarette distract you from your goal."

Trent told me that he threw the entire pack of cigarettes out the car window. Quitting smoking wasn't the only thing Trent needed to do to get in the kind of physical shape it takes to play pro hockey, but it sure as heck was a place to start.

Chapter Eight

The next morning I called Ron Sanko. Ron instructed us to meet him and coach Pete South at the Flint IMA Sports Arena at four p.m. in order to prepare for the Generals game against the now-defunct Bloomington Thunder.

I called Trent and told him the plan to meet Ron Sanko to pick up his jersey and uniform. "Do you want me to go with you, Trent?"

"Oh no, I can handle it myself," he said.

So Trent went up to Flint alone. Later he told me that when he arrived, Ron Sanko and Pete South walked up to him in the locker room while he was getting ready and said, "Well, Trent, you don't really look like a hockey player, but why don't you watch the game tonight, and tomorrow we'll put you in the lineup?"

Trent, being the nice guy that he is, said, "Well, okay, I'll sit tonight, and then tomorrow I'll be ready," even though they were screwing him over.

When Trent called to tell me what Ron Sanko and Pete South had said, I was super frustrated. "Ah jeez, Trent," I said. "I should have gone up there with you. They said they were gonna give you two games."

"I know, but those are the breaks," said Trent, always positive.

"Well, I tell you what," I said. "I'll come up and watch the game with you from the stands."

I was home with the wife and kids, but I knew I had to get up there. I couldn't let Trent get this close and not play. So I said, "Hey, honey, I'm going up to Flint for the weekend to watch the hockey game."

"Just like that?"

"Well, Trent was supposed to be playing in the game tonight, but they scratched him, and I'll be darned if that happens again tomorrow night." Luckily I have a great wife who always supports me, and she let me go to the game.

Chapter Nine

The Flint IMA Sports Arena is a rundown old place with a rusty exterior and beat-up seats in small town Michigan. But despite all that, it's a great place for hockey. Built in the 1960s and barely updated since, the arena seats four thousand hockey fans for the couple of minor league teams that call Flint home.

For the first game Trent attended, about 3,500 of those 4,000 seats were open. Trent and I sat right behind the home bench trying to size up the team. Maybe it was an off night or maybe it was not the Generals' year, but in either case, they couldn't get anything going in their direction that night. As the Generals fell to the final score of 6 to 1, I kept thinking, *This is total BS. Trent could skate circles around these clowns, and they're not even giving him a chance.*

After the final buzzer, I called Ron Sanko, who was sitting up in the press box. I said, "Hey, Ron, you know why you got your butt kicked tonight? Your best freaking player is sitting in the stands."

He laughed and said, "Hey, Jay, I'm sorry. Don't worry, your guy will get his shot tomorrow."

"Okay, Ron. I just thought I should let you know that Trent is better than every player you had on the ice tonight—on both teams!"

Still laughing, he said, "Well, we'll find out tomorrow, big guy."

Chapter Ten

The next afternoon in Flint, the Generals were scheduled to face off against Bloomington one more time. And sure enough, Trent was out there skating around for warm-ups. They had given him a jersey and put him in the lineup.

I sat in the stands and thought, *Holy cow, they put him out there on the ice without ever seeing him skate. Just based on what I told them.*

After watching Trent warm up, the game started, and he sat on the bench. The game was long, slogging, and boring, and by halfway through the second period, Trent hadn't even been on the ice once. I was getting livid in the stands. For the second day in a row, I watched these guys out there doing triple-luxes or whatever kind of loopty-loops while they got the crap beat out of them, and their best freakin' player sat right in front of me on the bench.

Trent sat fifty-nine eternal minutes until, with a minute left in the third period, the coach finally gave him his first freakin' shift. In that one minute Trent got a scoring chance, unlike what the rest of the team had been doing. The Generals wound up losing 2–1, with Trent sitting on the bench for all but enough time to take one shot at the goal.

After the game I talked to the coach, and he told me that he'd played Trent for only the last minute because the game was so tight. After Trent changed into his street clothes, the coach flagged him down in the hallway and said, "Hey Trent, thanks for coming out. I'm glad we could take a look at you. But we're not gonna keep you around this year. However, I'd like to invite you to our training camp next fall so you can come try out for our team. Have a good summer of training, and get in shape for next fall."

Trent told me what the coach had said. "I'd like to go back to Michigan Tech to finish my engineering degree, and then I'll get in shape for next fall."

"That sounds like a darn good plan, given the circumstances," I said.

Chapter Eleven

Trent went back to school, earned his bachelor's degree in structural engineering, graduated, and came home for the summer.

He started work as a structural engineer straight out of school. He also started working out on his own. He would run, and do push-ups and sit-ups. What he really needed to do to get to the next level was to bulk up. He was 155 to 165 pounds that summer, and most of the guys he would be squaring off against were up around 200 pounds. He wasn't exactly where he needed to be, but we headed into the fall confident nonetheless, with nothing to go on but Trent's natural talent on the ice.

Near the time we were expecting to hear about the details of the tryouts and get ready to go up to Flint, I got one of the most infuriating calls I've ever had in my life. It was Pete South, the coach of the Flint Generals, who I'd been talking to all summer about Trent going to the training camp.

"Hey, Jay," South said, "I'm sorry to tell you this, but Trent can't come to our training camp."

"Pete," I said, "what are you talking about? You've been telling me all summer . . ."

24

"Yeah, I know, I know, I feel super bad. But the thing is, the Red Wings are so loaded this year, their guys are gonna get filtered on to the Griffins, and the Griffins are loaded, and we're tied in to the Grand Rapids Griffins' farm system. So I don't see any way Trent could make the club. We've got more players as it is than we know what to do with, and we're going to be phenomenal. We're so good as it is, I don't see any reason for holding tryouts at all."

"Come on, Pete," I said. "Just let him try out. You already told him he could try out."

"Nope, nope, no! Your guy is not coming to my camp, Jay. That's the way it is," Pete said.

"Pete, how can you drop this bomb on me just a couple of weeks before the camp is supposed to start, when this kid has been training all summer long, and now you're screwing him over?"

"Well, Jay, that's not my problem; it's yours."

That's when I got livid and gave Pete South a piece of my mind. I told him about how it was baloney that just because the other players had gone to Division 1 schools and youth training camps, while Trent was dogging it out in the men's leagues, didn't mean anything when it came game time.

Well, maybe he heard enough of my yapping and wanted to change the subject, or maybe he started to feel bad for letting us down in such a rotten fashion, but either way, Pete South did wind up helping us out.

Interrupting my rant, Pete said, "I tell you what, Jay, I'm going to try to do something for you."

"Something? The Generals was our shot! I don't have any connections. This is the one chance for this extreme talent to play in front of some people that are smart enough to know how good he is."

"Okay, Jay. Just give me a couple days to see if I can figure something out."

A couple days later Pete South called me back and told me about a new team starting in the Eastern Professional Hockey League. They would be the Rome Copper City Chiefs located in Rome, New York. "A good friend of mine, Mike Beavis, is going to be coaching them. I called Mike and he said he could use Trent on his team. And I tell you what, if Trent goes over there and dominates, we'll call him up to the Flint Generals. The Chiefs will be a good place for him to start, because they're single A and we're double A, and I think it will be the perfect spot for Trent to start his pro career."

"Well, okay, Pete, what do I gotta do now?" "First thing, call Mike Beavis." He gave me Beavis's phone number.

"All right, Pete, thanks for working something out."

Chapter Twelve

As soon as I got off the phone with Pete South, I called Mike Beavis of the Rome Copper City Chiefs.

"Jay," he said, "I heard about you, and I'm excited to see Trent and see what he can do. We've got a great ownership group . . ."

Mike and I talked for a while. We hit it off, bonding over the fact that we both have big families—I was the oldest of nine siblings and Pete had seven kids. We were both excited to get Trent over to New York so the team could get ready for the start of their first season.

After I got off the phone with Mike Beavis, the next step was to call Trent. This was going to be a tough phone call because I had yet to tell Trent that Pete South had called and canceled Trent's tryouts with the Generals. But at least I had gotten him in with another team.

So I called Trent up and said, "Listen, buddy, the Generals screwed us over again. They're not even gonna let you try out. I'm so sorry. I'm sick to my stomach that they could let that happen. But when one door closes, another one opens, and now I got you in with a brand new team, over in Rome, New York."

"Okay," Trent said, unwavering in his commitment to the game of hockey, "what's this new team all about?"

"They're called the Rome Copper City Chiefs. I just got off the phone with their coach, Mike Beavis. He's a great guy, and he's heard all about you. He wants you to go play for him. And Pete South said if you go down there and dominate, they'll call you up to the Generals. He said that Rome will be a good place to kick your career off."

"Okay, Jay, that's not a problem," Trent said. "Just let me know what I've got to do."

"You've got it, man, Just keep working out, and I'm going to take care of the rest. Give me a couple weeks and I'll call you back with your flight information."

"Okay, that sounds good," Trent replied.

"You ready to go?"

"I'll be ready."

We were both super excited to get another lifeline. Trent was working out, and I had told my wife that I would be flying out to the East Coast any day. Well, you wouldn't believe what happen next—another ridiculous obstacle.

Mike Beavis called me up two weeks later and said, "Jay, I hate to tell you this, but I just got off the phone with the owner, and he's folding the team." I groaned into the phone. "We're not going to have a team this year."

"You have got to be kidding me!"

He talked about how disappointed he was, going on about how he was now jobless with seven kids, and how excited he had been to see Trent play and win some games. Mike Beavis was a nice guy, but he didn't help us out that day.

I was back to the drawing board. Starting over from square one with just my phone to rely on, a lot like the first day I started my insurance business. And as with my business, I wasn't about to give up just because we'd gotten knocked down.

Chapter Thirteen

I wondered what my next move would be. I wasn't sure exactly where to turn next, so I called an old friend of mine who knew a ton about pro hockey, Tim, to tell him our story, hoping some lightbulbs would turn on.

After I told Tim about Trent, I said, "Well, the Flint Generals screwed us over, and then this Rome Copper City Chiefs deal fell through. Now I'm just not sure what to do."

"I hear you, Jay," said Tim. "It's tough for kids trying to get their pro-hockey career started, even coming out of college or the OHL, let alone a men's league."

"Yeah, I understand that. But no one has even seen this kid, Tim. Somebody's at least got to give him a shot."

"I tell you what, Jay. I know Bob McNamara, the general manager of the Grand Rapids Griffins. Let me give him a call and tell him about Trent."

"Okay, Tim. That sounds good. Let me know if you can pull some strings."

"Okay, Jay. And in the meantime, don't give up."

With that little word of encouragement, I got the motivation to start making cold calls again to see if I could get Trent an in somewhere. I started calling every number related to pro hockey that I could possibly dial. I called Nick Bootland, coach of the Kalamazoo Wings; Jarrod Skalde, coach of the Bloomington Prairie Thunder; Bruce Ramsay of the Muskegon Lumberjacks; Al Sims of the Ft. Wayne Komets; and Stan Drulia with the Port Huron Icehawks. I called every team in the IHL, every team in the ECHL, and every team in every pro hockey league you can think of, including a team called the New Jersey Grasshoppers—anyone I thought might possibly give us a chance—nonstop for a week straight. For days I kept getting the same response: "You've got to be kidding me. This kid is playing in men's leagues? Are you crazy? What kinda nut job are you? We're a pro hockey team. We can't look at a kid playing in a men's league."

Chapter Fourteen

A week later we finally saw some daylight when I got a call back from Tim.

Tim told me that he had talked to Bob McNamara, and Bob was getting his team ready for a practice at Joe Louis Arena, home of the Detroit Red Wings. Bob McNamara had invited Trent to go down to Detroit and skate with the Griffins, the Red Wings top farm team.

"That's awesome!" I said, super excited. "Thanks a million. When does Trent need to be there?"

"You've got to get him down there by one o'clock tomorrow."

"That's great. Do you think it'd be all right if I went to watch?" I'd be darned if Trent was to be swept off to the side again under my watch, so I wanted to make sure I was there to represent him if need be.

"Well, the practice is closed to the public, but let me check in with Bobby Mac and we'll see what we can do."

A few minutes later Tim called me back and told me I could go down to Detroit to watch Trent practice with the Griffins.

After I got off the phone with Tim, I immediately called Trent. "Guess what? You're going to get to skate for Bob McNamara, general manager of the Grand Rapids Griffins. It's another chance for someone to get a look at you."

"Oh, that's sweet. Thanks!" Trent said.

"You've got to be down to Joe Louis Arena by one o'clock tomorrow."

"Joe Louis Arena. Yeah, that's sound great. Of course I'll be there."

"All right. I'll be there to watch the practice."

"Sweet! Sounds great. See you then!"

Chapter Fifteen

It's not every day you get to see the inside of Joe Louis Arena when it's closed to the public, so I got down there a little early to check out the sights. It sure is a different feel when those twenty thousand seats are empty and no long lines filter around the concession stands or bathrooms. Everything is way quieter. You don't hear any horns or music, and a lot of the lights are off. I sat down a little way up the bench with Bob McNamara and Tim to watch the guys come out on the ice. Ten other people sat in the stands.

Trent got out there on the Detroit Red Wings' ice with all these phenomenal hockey players—guys who were all one step away from the NHL. They skated around, doing the normal cookie-cutter drills—two on ones, battle drills, small area games, stuff like that—and Trent did not look out of place one bit. He made nice passes, set guys up, and put it on the tape. He looked darn good.

McNamara nodded his head. "Hey, this kid's pretty good. He can really handle himself out there, from what I've seen so far."

I then noticed, a few rows in front of us, none other than Pete South, the guy who had denied Trent tryouts with the Flint Generals just a few weeks prior.

A few minutes later, Pete South turned around and said, "Hey Bobby, who's that number 7 out there?"

Lo and behold, who was number 7? Why none other than Trent Daavettila. Boy, that sure got me. I yelled down, "Hey Pete, you know who that is? That's Trent Daavettila, the guy you turned away from tryouts last month. Take a look out of your good eye, buddy!"

Tim elbowed me in the chest. "Hey, hey. Jay, you've got to calm down."

"Oh come on, Tim! Trent busted his butt all summer, and that guy screwed him over."

Bob McNamara glanced over at me and said, "You know what? I kinda get where you're coming from, Jay. Some guys don't always get it right."

After practice was over, Bobby McNamara and I chatted in the hall outside the locker room where a bunch of plaques hung with all the greatest players from Red Wings history engraved on them, as well as a mural of all eleven of the Detroit Stanley Cups painted on the wall. Trent approached us with his hockey bags draped over his shoulder. Bobby Mac said, "Hey Trent, you looked good out there today. So what I'm thinking is that I'm going to give a call up to Muskegon and get you a tryout for the Lumberjacks. I think my friend Bruce Ramsay can find a place for you up there."

Trent looked at us with a huge grin, tired from practice and lugging around all his equipment. "OK," he said, his whole face smiling. After all the ups and downs with Pete South and the Flint Generals, it felt pretty darn good that Bobby recognized Trent's talent.

Chapter Sixteen

On my way driving back from Joe Louis Arena, I started working the phones again, calling three or four managers of other minor league teams. Now that Bruce Ramsay was interested, I had a brand new sales pitch. I rattled on about Trent's practice with the Grand Rapids Griffins. They didn't seem to believe that Trent had been invited to skate with the Griffins. "You'd better believe the Griffins are looking at Trent. He more than kept up with their regular players. At least Bobby McNamara thought so!" For the whole hour-long drive from Joe Louis Arena to my place, I went on about Trent to these managers. "Now he's got a tryout with the Muskegon Lumberjacks, and when he gets signed, don't come crying to me because you missed the boat on this one!"

I gave my pitch to Jarrod Skalde, who coached the Bloomington Thunder of the IHL. "The Grand Rapids Griffins looked at Trent?" Skalde said, sounding shocked and surprised.

"You better believe it!" Skalde had a heck of pro career as a player, playing center for a few different teams throughout, so I had to respect him for that.

Skalde said, "Listen, Jay, just give me a few days and let me think about this."

"I'm telling you, Skalde, time's running short on someone signing this kid. You might end up regretting not jumping on it right now." I could tell he was thinking about it on the other end of the line.

Chapter Seventeen

Later that week I was online watching Pete South's Flint Generals play the Fort Wayne Komets—I wanted to size up this "loaded" Generals team that was too good to let Trent in for a tryout. And darn it if the Generals didn't look like a bunch of cows skating around on the pond in the backyard—I was beginning to wonder what the heck Pete South meant by "loaded."

The next morning I called up Pete South and said, "Man, so you remember when you told me that Trent couldn't try out with the Generals because you guys were loaded? Well, I watched your game versus the Komets last night—you know, the one where you lost eleven to one — —and you guys sure as heck didn't look loaded to me. So listen, Pete, judging by everything that I've seen and heard, I've come to one of two conclusions: either your team is "loaded" with public skaters, or you're a terrible hockey coach. It's one of the two. And my guess is it's the latter. If your team keeps playing like they did last night, you're going to be out of a job shortly." After I spoke my mind, I hung up the phone in utter frustration.

As it turned out, a short time after that call, I got word that Pete South had been replaced as head coach, validating my belief that if he didn't have the wherewithal to recognize Trent's talents, then he probably wasn't suited to be a pro hockey coach.

A few days after telling Pete South off, I got a call from my friend Tim. "Jay," he said, "Bobby McNamara wants to talk to you. You guys are getting a tryout in Muskegon."

So I got on the phone with Bobby, and he said, "Yeah Jay, I talked to Bruce Ramsay, the coach of the Muskegon Lumberjacks—he's a good friend of mine—and I told him all about the practice Trent had with us down at Joe Louis Arena. He wants Trent to go up there to Muskegon for a three-day tryout."

"Thank you, Bobby. That sounds great," I said. I hung up the phone with Bobby and called Trent.

When Trent picked up the phone, I could tell he was still tired from the last practice, so I start pumping him up for the Muskegon tryout. "Yeah, bud, I just got off the phone with Bruce Ramsay, coach of the Muskegon Lumberjacks. They want you up there for a three-day tryout."

"Jeez, Jay, that's awesome," he said.

"You better believe it. You feeling ready for the next level?"

"In all honesty, Jay, I'm pretty darn tired from that last skate around, but it felt good. I was making plays, getting around guys, and I want to get out there and do it again."

Tired or not, we had no time to spare.

Trent went up to Muskegon by himself to do the tryouts, but the results were not what we had hoped for.

This tryout in Muskegon was where it truly became obvious that Trent was going to have to get into some kind of training program if he was ever going to come into his own as a hockey player. That summer he had been working forty-plus hour weeks as an engineer, running and doing sit-ups on his days off, eating whatever he wanted, and perhaps still smoking cigarettes on occasion, which was nuts, in retrospect. No professional athlete would think of being a regular smoker in this day and age.

In any case, after three days trying out in Muskegon, I got a call from Trent. "Hey, Jay, bad news. Bruce Ramsay just cut me."

"Oh jeez, Trent. That doesn't make a whole lot of sense to me. What the heck happened up there?"

"Tell you the truth, I'm not feeling so good."

"How's that?"

"I'm just exhausted. Feels like I've been moving eighty-pound sandbags around for the last week straight. My muscles are sore, and I just want to get in bed."

"Jeez, don't get down on yourself. Listen, Bruce Ramsay doesn't know what he's looking at. What you need to do is get geared up to get in better shape and start thinking about your next tryout."

"Ok, we'll see," said Trent, sounding a little dejected.

"Darn it, Trent," I said, frustrated that he sounded so down on himself. "It's not 'we will see,' it is what we see. And what we see is a shot playing in the NHL in your future. Don't forget that—keep your eye on the prize; it's only a few steps away."

"I'm ready, Jay. Believe me, I'll be ready."

Chapter Eighteen

After getting cut by Bruce Ramsay at the Muskegon tryouts, Trent may have been feeling unmotivated, but as for me, I sure as heck wasn't slowing down. After Trent called to tell me he was cut, I got right on the phone looking for our next opportunity.

I called Nick Bootland, who was the new head coach of the Kalamazoo Wings starting that year. "Hey Nick," I said, "you've got to take a look at this kid, Trent Daavettila. Grand Rapids is interested in him, and a few other teams have been sniffing around too. But Trent and I both are personally big fans of the K-Wings. I think Kalamazoo would be a good place for Trent to get his start."

"Well, I don't know, Jay," said Nick. "We don't typically look at guys playing in men's leagues—in fact we never do, to my knowledge. How good is this kid?"

"Jeez, Nick, come on. Would the Grand Rapids Griffins be inviting him to try out at Joe Louis Arena if he wasn't any good? Listen, Nick, you and Trent are in pretty similar positions. It's your first year coaching, and it's Trent's first year playing. Now somebody must have given you a shot at coaching. Why don't you do yourself a favor and give Trent a shot at playing? He doesn't have a big-time resume, but the kid's an unbelievable hockey player. And just like someone took a chance on you as a rookie coach, I need you to take a chance on a rookie pond rocket. Because he's gonna make you look like a genius."

Well, I must have said something right, because Nick said, "All right, all right, call me back in a few days."

After I hung up with Nick, I picked the phone right back up, called Jarrod Skalde, and gave him the same speech. And then I called Al Sims in Fort Wayne and gave him the same speech. And I kept calling guys and giving them the same speech. I had about every minor league hockey team in the country talking about Trent within a few days. I called and called and called, until I was sure that everyone had the bug in their ear about Trent.

Finally, after a month of talking to guys—sometimes the same guy three, four times a week, and hearing every excuse in the book for why they couldn't bring Trent in for a tryout—I got an in with Bootland and the K-Wings.

"Come on, Nick, just let him come out and skate with you guys," I said plainly.

"Jay, to be quite frank, I'm sick and tired of you calling me all the time. If this is what it will take for you to quit calling me, your guy can come out and skate. I'll take a look at him, and we'll see what he can do," said Nick. "On one condition, though. If I cut him, I won't hear any complaints from you, and you'll quit calling me."

"Nick, I understand. I'm persistent, but I also know what I'm talking about. I guarantee you, he's not gonna look out of place. He's going to make the K-Wings better, and he's gonna make you a better hockey coach."

"Okay, Jay. Then I'm looking forward to seeing him tomorrow morning. I want him here at nine a.m. for practice."

Chapter Nineteen

After I got off the phone with Nick Bootland, I called Trent right away. "Trent, you'd better get ready because you have to be in Kalamazoo at nine for a tryout tomorrow morning."

"Okay, sounds good," said Trent.

"That's right, Trent. This is a good shot here. You've got to get up and out of your place at seven in the morning, because you have an hour and a half drive tomorrow. And make sure you get some good rest."

Three days later, I got a call from Bootland. "You're right, Jay. Trent's a pretty darn good player, but we're pretty full right now. I'm going to keep you guys on the back burner in case we get an injury."

"Okay, Nick," I said, "but you may miss your shot. This kid's getting some interest from other teams right now."

"I know, Jay. I can see his talent," said Nick, "but as I said, we're pretty full. Let's just wait and see."

"Okay, Nick. I'm sure we'll be talking again."

Chapter Twenty

I spoke to Trent on his way back from Kalamazoo. "Listen, buddy, we don't have time to slack. I've got a couple irons in the fire, and I'm gonna keep working them. You're going to be playing somewhere, soon. We just need to be patient and stay the course."

So I got back on the phone, calling the same coaches over and over again. Three weeks later, I got a call back from Jarrod Skalde. And wouldn't you know it, Skalde said pretty much the same thing Bootland did. "Jay, I'm sick and tired of you calling me all the time. If it will get you off my back, I'll give the kid a shot." And all of that same chin-wagging until I had a deal worked out to send Trent down to Bloomington to try out with the Prairie Thunder.

I called Trent and told him he was going to try out down in Bloomington. "You've got to leave tomorrow. They want you the day after."

"You've got it, Jay. I'll start getting ready right now."

I started thinking about Trent's old, beat-up truck—he had this rust bucket that must have been older than him, with the tailgate stuck in place and tape over one of the headlights. I started thinking about him driving that thing all the way down to Illinois and getting worried that he'd break down alongside the highway, missing his opportunity. So I said, "Trent, you've got a car that can make it that far?"

"You're right, Jay. I'll talk to my dad about borrowing his car."

"What car is that, Trent?"

"He'll probably let me take the big van." Well, Trent has eleven siblings, so when he said big van, he meant a twelve-passenger van.

"The extendo-van?" I clarified, surprised.

"Yeah, Jay," Trent said, chuckling.

"Trent, you're going to Illinois to try out for a pro hockey team. You don't take a frickin' twelve-passenger van to Bloomington—they'll think you're a frickin' weirdo. Screw that, you're taking my car."

"Ah, jeez, Jay, that's nice, but I don't want to inconvenience you."

"Don't give me that, Trent. I'm parking my car in your drive and then I'm going to run home. The keys will be in the ignition."

Chapter Twenty-One

Trent went down to Bloomington, and after three days I got this sense of déjà vu when he called me up to say, "Skalde cut me."

"Oh, come on! You've got to be kidding me. What did he say exactly?"

"He thinks I'm too small, Jay."

"Oh, come on!"

"That's what he said. He also told me that I'm good and he can see what you've been yapping about, but he's worried about me getting hurt."

"What a bunch of crap! Trent, listen, if he said all that, something inside of him is telling him that he's not 100 percent sure. Here's what I want you to do—put on your big boy pants and walk into his office and say, 'Skalde, I want you to look at me again. I ain't leaving for another week,' and see what he said."

"Oh jeez, I don't know, Jay," Trent said humbly.

"Trent, do it exactly like I said. Walk into his office and say, 'I'm not leaving because I think you're wrong, and I want you to give me another week.' Trent, you've got to do it. I could do it for you, but sometimes you've got to do what you've got to do. And I'm telling you, if I was the coach and a kid did that to me, I would tell him he could stay another week."

"Okay, Jay, I'll give it a shot," Trent said, hanging up.

A half-hour later Trent called me back and said, "Jay, I did exactly what you said, and Skalde said I could stay another week."

"Sweet!" I said, all excited. "That's a huge step you just took right there, buddy!"

"I know. I was kinda nervous going in there, but I sure am glad I did."

"I know, but this isn't about embarrassing yourself; this is about getting your chance."

Trent chuckled a bit and said, "I know, you give me confidence to do this kinda stuff."

"I know. That's why I'm your agent. That's my job."

Chapter Twenty-Two

Trent tried out with Bloomington for another week, but Skalde still cut him. Well, that just about blew me away. Something was missing out of this puzzle. Why the heck weren't these guys seeing the obvious talent like I was?

When Trent came home a day later, he was pretty down on himself. "Listen," I said, trying to pump him back up, "don't worry about anything. These guys are wrong."

I didn't waste any time getting back on the phone, this time with Stan Drulia, the head coach of the Port Huron Icehawks at the time. Drulia agreed to a tryout.

At this point it was January, about halfway through the season. Trent had been busting his butt at his engineer job forty hours a week and trying to get in shape in between. He didn't have much time for real training, though, and he still looked small compared to a lot of the other guys.

So he drove up to Port Huron, two and half hours away from his parents' house. He arrived at McMorran Arena, a small hockey stadium that seats 3,400 a few blocks from the St. Clair River and the Canadian border, and parked his car in the old parking lot with cracked-up pavement next to the seven or eight cars there for practice that day. Trent was getting all his gear out of the trunk when Stan Drulia came out of the arena and approached him.

"Daavettila?" said Stan.

"Yes, sir, you must be Stan Drulia. Nice to meet you," said Trent.

"So, you're Trent Daavettila—the guy Jay Storm has been screaming and hollering about the last few months," said Stan, sizing up Trent.

"That's right."

"Listen, Trent, I'm not letting you out on the ice."

"What's that?" said Trent, a bit shocked.

"Now that I see you, I get why you're not on a pro team already. You're not big enough for this league. You'd get killed if I put you out on the ice. I can't do that to you."

"Well, Stan, I've been driving up here all morning to get a chance to skate for you. I'd like to at least get out on the ice for a tryout."

"Listen, Trent. This isn't your fault. Jay is nuts. What are you, like 170 pounds?"

"One sixty-five, actually."

"One sixty-five! Seriously? Yep, that settles it—Jay is completely off his rocker. Listen, Trent, I hate to be the one to say this, but you should stick to playing recreational hockey. This is a big boy's league, and my job is to make sure you don't get hurt. So you might as well go home, because I ain't letting you on the ice today."

Trent was upset. Over the last few months he'd been to Muskegon, Bloomington, Kalamazoo, and Flint, and despite all these coaches and managers acknowledging his skills, he seemed to lack something that was only about appearance.

After Trent called me to give me the bad news, I called Drulia up to try to figure out what his deal was, but he didn't pick up the phone.

I never did talk to Stan Drulia again after that.

Chapter Twenty-Three

"I'm not gonna quit till you get a chance," I told Trent as he drove home from Port Huron, making sure he didn't get down on himself again. "Don't worry about those guys. Someone is gonna recognize your talent yet. Don't give up."

"OK, Jay, I hear you," said Trent. "I really appreciate everything you're doing for me right now. But I'm frustrated as heck—Drulia didn't even let me get on the ice!"

"Drulia is just a minor bump in the road. Don't worry about it, we'll have a real tryout for you right quick," I said, and then added, "Listen, Trent. Don't worry about any of this right now. We had a tough break, but there's somebody out there who is gonna help you take that next step toward the NHL, and it's my job to find that person. So hold tight while I do my job. You just be ready to go when you get the call."

I got off the phone with Trent and started calling every minor league hockey team I could think of. I made sure everyone in the IHL—the minor league in our area—knew the name Trent Daavettila. I probably called seventy coaches over those next few weeks looking for that one guy who was going to say yes. I wanted so badly to make that call to

Trent to say that I had found the one who was going to give him the shot, but first I had to find that person.

Meanwhile I watched K-Wings games on the Internet, and other IHL teams as well, to see if they got any injuries or any spots opened up. After a couple guys got knocked out, I called up the K-Wings coach, Nick Bootland.

At this point Bootland was pretty sick of hearing from me, and it took him awhile to pick up his phone. But after about fifty messages and emails, I finally got through to him.

"Come on, Bootland," I said, "you've got to put him out there on the ice during a game. You've only seen this kid skating loop and shoot during practice. You've got to see him play in a game, man! I've watched ten K-Wings games online, and your team is full of public skaters. They skate around like chicken with their head cut off, but they don't get anything done on the ice, as far as production goes."

Bootland chuckled a bit and said, "We'll see."

"One more thing, Nick. I just wanna tell you something—Trent is a seven o'clocker, not a two o'clocker."

"What do you mean?"

"Some guys look good skating around cones at two o'clock in the afternoon, during practice. And other guys look good at seven o'clock game time, when it matters. Trent's a seven o'clocker. Remember that."

Bootland chuckled again and said, "I might have something for him shortly."

A week of silence followed. I finally got a call back on a Tuesday night. "Hey, Jay," said Bootland. "What's Trent doing tomorrow?"

"Open schedule tomorrow, Nick. What do you have for him?" I asked.

"We've got an education day game tomorrow morning against Port Huron. Do you think he can make it?"

"Yes," I said.

"Well, it's gonna be a pretty fun game. The local schools are bussing in kids, and there's gonna be a bunch of eight-year-olds screaming at the top of their lungs at ten o'clock in the morning. It'll be a fun experience for Trent. I can't tell you how much ice time he'll get, but a couple guys went down last week and we need a body."

"Sounds good! Listen, Nick, will you do me a favor, though, and call Trent to let him know? I think it's time he heard from you directly that you want him on the ice."

"Okay, Jay. Fair enough. I'll give him a call."

After I hung up with Bootland, I looked at the K-Wings schedule and saw that they had twenty games left in their season—plenty enough time for Trent to make his mark, if he could only stick.

Chapter Twenty-Four

I'm glad I had that idea to have Nick Bootland call Trent himself, because it did exactly what I was hoping it would—got Trent all fired up to go over to Kalamazoo and play. Trent called me up a few minutes after he got off the phone with Bootland, "Guess what, Jay? I just got a call from Nick Bootland, and he wants me to go over to Kalamazoo tomorrow to play in an educational day game."

"That's awesome, Trent! Congratulations. See what happens when you never give up? You're getting a break now, so let's try to make the most of this opportunity."

"Heck yeah, Jay! I'm super pumped."

The next morning I drove to Kalamazoo to watch the game. Sure enough, Trent was out on the ice in front of a pretty decent crowd. He got two shifts in the first period, one in the second, and two in the third period, so five shifts total, probably a total of two minutes ice time. Well, the K-Wings lost 2–0 to Port Huron. It was clear to me, the way Trent looked in those five shifts, that he could have gotten at least a couple scoring chances had they given him more ice time.

During that final period I got pretty darn upset watching the K-Wings overlooking Trent's talents. It made no sense to me that they weren't playing him. As the clock ticked down to the final buzzer, I got up near the glass and hollered at the bench, "Hey coach, you want to score some goals? Why don't you try playing your best frickin' player?"

After the game, I called up Nick Bootland and said, "Nick, why didn't you play the kid when you guys were down out there? You want to score goals, don't you? Trent's the best player on your team right now."

"Jay, he's good," said Nick, "but he's a pretty small dude compared to some of those other guys, and I'm worried about him getting hurt."

"Nick, if you're worried about him getting hurt, then you don't deserve to have him on your team. Trent's not in the best shape right now, but he can hold his own. And besides, those big goons out there probably would never be able touch him. Just put him on a good line and give him some ice time."

"Well, I'm actually going to keep him around for the weekend," said Nick. "We've got a game Friday night, and a couple of our guys are still banged up, so he's going to get some ice time then."

"Okay, Nick, that sounds good."

Chapter Twenty-Five

After the educational day game, Trent figured he was getting cut again. When Bootland called him to let him know he'd be staying through the weekend and getting more ice time, Trent was pumped.

Trent stayed in Kalamazoo for the remainder of that week. That Thursday they had a late practice, so Trent skated around with them to get ready for Friday's game.

Friday night the K-Wings went up against the Flint Generals, with a familiar face, Pete South, as the Generals coach. Finally, after being denied tryouts by Pete earlier in the season, Trent was gonna get a chance to show him what he was all about.

It was a pretty big crowd on Friday night at the K-Wings stadium, and the players were pumped up. I sat right behind the bench and watched Kalamazoo go down four to one in the second period.

At that point Trent had only gotten two shifts. The K-Wings second line center—a guy named Anthony Battaglia—was handling most of the shifts, even though he wasn't getting many scoring chances.

The K-Wings appeared to be working their way to another loss with Trent sitting on the bench. Then about halfway through the second period, Battaglia went into the corner with a huge defenseman and got completely creamed. Battaglia was knocked out of the game with a separated shoulder.

Luckily Battaglia wasn't hurt worse than a separated shoulder, but he was out nonetheless, and therefore a window of opportunity opened. I got up against the glass and pounded and yelled at Bootland, "Play him, coach. Come on; now's the time!"

Bootland looked at me and nodded, then he tapped Trent on the shoulder and said, "Hey, Daavettila, it's time to show me what you've got. You're going to be centering the second line for the rest of the game."

After the injured Battaglia got off the ice, Trent went out for his first shift and nothing much happened. Time was beginning to wind down in the second period when Trent got another shift that went much the same as the first.

On the third shift late in the second period, Trent got going. He broke down ice, dodged a defenseman, and set up a beautiful goal to make it four to two. I pounded on the glass, cheering and yelling, "I told you, Bootland! Keep sending him over the boards!"

As the third period started, the arena was buzzing with anticipation. The K-Wings had momentum and were starting to look like they might tie it up. Trent went out for his fourth shift and did a good job keeping possession and passing around. Trent sat while the third line and then the first line took their shifts. When Trent went out for his next shift, he scored the tying goal! The Friday night crowd went nuts, and people started asking about the new kid out on the ice. "That's Trent Daavettila," I said. "You watch him. This kid is going places!"

The K-Wings had the momentum, and they scored one more goal a few minutes before the final buzzer to win the game. The game was an ideal first for Trent, who had a goal and an assist to beat Pete South's Generals.

As the final seconds were counting down in that game, I couldn't resist going over to the Generals bench. I walked right up behind Pete South and railed on the glass. "Hey, coach! How do you like Daavettila now, huh? You still think he's not good enough for your *loaded* team? Not good enough for a tryout, huh? Who just beat the crap out of you guys? Trent Daavettila, that's who! Not bad for a pond rocket, hey boys? And don't you forget it when you're out of a job next season!"

Yeah, it wasn't the most sportsmanlike thing to do, but at that point, I didn't mind rubbing it in Pete South's face.

Chapter Twenty-Six

After the big win, I called up Nick Bootland and said, "What do you think now, baby? You're going to be watching this kid on TV someday soon, man! Keep playing him."

"Hey, Jay, I don't know if it's beginners luck or what, but I want Trent to stick around for another game."

"Well, you're darn right you want him sticking around. Maybe it's time to talk about a longer contract?"

"Let's keep Trent on the ice the next few games and sort of play it by ear. Don't push it, Jay. Let's just see how it plays out. Believe me, I want Trent to be as good as he looked last night, too. And if he's that good, I feel confident he'll be playing a lot more pro hockey."

The next night the K-Wings were scheduled to play the Fort Wayne Komets. The K-Wings lost 4–1, but Trent scored the lone goal.

I called Bootland again after the Fort Wayne game and said, "How are you going to cut this kid? He's got three points over two games, and essentially that was just a game and a half, because you didn't even really play him the first game. How would you cut him?"

"Jay, you're right," said Bootland. "I'm not cutting him right now. My guys are getting healthy, but as long as Trent keeps producing like this, he's not going anywhere."

"Hey Nick, this party is just getting started. You haven't seen nothing yet," I said.

"Jay, this little bugger is good."

"Well, what the heck do you think I've been telling you that for?"

"I'm actually getting pretty excited about him," said Bootland.

"You'd better be, because he's going to lead your team to the play-offs. Just keep playing him. Trust me."

Chapter Twenty-Seven

Trent played hard the rest of that season with the K-Wings. He started getting more and more ice time, and gaining the respect of the coaches and other players.

He was working harder than any other time in his life. The physical endurance it takes to play one game in the IHL was way beyond anything Trent had ever seen in men's leagues. And being new to the league, not coming from any special training background, he had to make a number of adjustments quite quickly.

For instance, Trent's equipment looked like something forgotten in an old, neglected toolshed. He had old beat-up skates held together with duct tape, for crying out loud! Those first few games he complained as much as the day is long about his feet and leg muscles. So I went out and bought him some new skates. Despite some better equipment, Trent was still woozy and tired after every game, but at least we all felt we were moving in the right direction.

Throughout that last twenty games of the season with the K-Wings, we realized that some component of Trent's training was clearly missing. He'd call me up and tell me about how the other players were out on the bikes in between games, hitting the weight room, all while he continued to worked part time as an engineer.

Trent's engineering work slowed down, and he got temporarily laid off, which may have been a blessing in disguise. Because he was free from work for a few months, he dedicated all of his time to playing hockey, and then we really started to see what it was going to take to get to the next level.

Trent played great that first season, no doubt about that. In the twenty games he played, he scored eighteen points—nine goals and nine assists. And he didn't even have any power play minutes! Trent's numbers were some of the best in the IHL for those twenty games. The K-Wings went to the play-offs, but they didn't have the best all-around team and were knocked out in the first round. Nevertheless, Trent had cemented himself as a center forward with a ton of promise.

Chapter Twenty-Eight

As the season approached the end, I began to evaluate what was preventing Trent from being as good as his pure talent would allow him to be. He wasn't short on talent, that much was clear. He was able to produce points nearly as well as anybody on the ice. Trent had the ability to see every player on the ice at the same time. He'd be down in the offensive zone with the puck, surrounded by three defenders, and with only the thinnest margin for error, slip the puck between them all to his teammate in the complete opposite direction that he was looking. It was like Trent had eyes in the back of his head. He had played like that ever since he started in peewees, and now was playing the same way in the IHL.

Despite his unique vision, some questions remained about Trent as a player at the pro level. These questions primarily surrounded his size. That first season with the K-Wings, he weighed 165 pounds, and if he was a true six feet tall in stocking feet, I'd be surprised. A lot of the guys he was going up against were six feet plus and over two hundred pounds. Trent was quick, but his size and strength were clearly issues.

Trent's next step in development would be to get a trainer—somebody who could develop him enough physically to handle the rigors of a full hockey season, and would know the correct path to get Trent's unique physique into top-level shape.

Chapter Twenty-Nine

I started talking to people about trainers. Eventually I heard about Chris Ramberg, who lived in the area. Chris was a young trainer at the time and pretty low-key, making a name for himself training young hockey players who were headed to the pros.

Chris hadn't gone to school for training and wasn't part of a big facility or pro team. But he had wanted to be a trainer ever since he was a kid. He grew up in a hockey family and his big brother played for the junior Red Wings.

Like Trent, Chris had good instincts. He told me he grew up idolizing Bruce Lee and read all about the martial artist's famous training methods when he was a teenager. From there, Chris began to develop his own unique training program that could be adjusted according to each client's needs.

Hearing all this about Chris, I got pretty excited, so I called him up to see if he would be willing to work with Trent that summer. I got Chris on the phone a week before the season ended. "Hey, Chris. This is Jay Storm," I said. "I heard you've got a pretty unique training program, and I'm looking for a trainer."

"Hello there, Jay. Thanks for getting in touch," Chris said. "That's true I'm a trainer and I did design my own program, so I'd say it's unique."

"I've heard you're a natural when it comes to training."

"I suppose you could say that," said Chris.

"That's good, because the guy who needs to get in shape is a natural too."

"Is that so?"

"Yeah, it's a pretty unique situation," I said. "Trent is a hockey player who got cut in college at Michigan Tech, so he started playing recreational hockey, and now he's advanced on to the IHL. He's been playing with the Kalamazoo Wings, but he needs to get stronger over the summer."

"Is that so?"

"Yep, he's got the natural gifts to play at any level. That I'm sure of, but we've got to bulk him up and get him into shape. Do you think you'd want to work with Trent this summer?"

"Well, sounds pretty good so far, Jay. Why don't you guys come by my facility in Brighton and we can talk things over."

"All right, where at in Brighton?"

"It's actually at my house, Jay."

"Your house?"

"Yep, I've got everything we need right in my basement."

"Well, heck, that sounds all right. I'll let you know when we're coming."

"Sounds good."

I called Trent as he was resting in between games. "Trent, I'm sick of you moaning and groaning about being sore after games," I said, joking around. "What we've got to do is get you in some sort of training program this summer." "Oh, jeez, Jay. I'd love to have a trainer to work with. A bunch of other guys on the team are always talking about their trainers. But I can't afford that. I'd be lucky if I can even afford gas this summer, seeing as I don't have a job right now."

"Forget about that, bud," I said. "I already got that part figured out. You're going to be training six days a week like an animal. You up for it?"

"Heck yeah, I'm up for it! But are you sure you want to do all that?"

"Of course I want to! I'm your agent, and I'll be darned if you're not in tip-top shape come next fall. I've already talked to a guy named Chris Ramberg. He wants us to go down to his place. He's got a training facility in his basement, and he comes highly recommended."

"Okay, Jay, that sounds pretty good," said Trent.

Chapter Thirty

The next time Trent had a couple days off, we went down to Chris Ramberg's place. I could tell right away that Chris was dedicated to training. He was in good shape himself, and he was laser focused on the project at hand. Right away he said to Trent, "Boy, what have you been eating all winter, cornflakes?"

"Pretty much," said Trent.

"You're not eating enough protein, I can tell that just from looking at you. What do you weigh, around 150 pounds?"

"Err, 165," said Trent, looking a little embarrassed.

"Boy, you're going to need to put on some weight if you're going to play pro hockey. No wonder everybody's saying your talent is bigger than you are."

"Sounds good!" said Trent.

Then Chris showed us around his training facilities, which were all the bare necessities packed into a finished basement—jump ropes, punching bags, weights, a squat rack, stuff like that. Chris told us about his background and training style, and I could see Trent liked what he was hearing. Right away, Chris seemed like a guy who could keep Trent focused on getting to the next level for the upcoming season.

So I said, "Gentleman, let's do it this summer!" And we agreed to start a week after the season ended.

Trent's engineering work picked back up that summer, and he started working fifty-hour weeks, but that didn't stop him from training. He just had to work extra hard. He'd show up at Chris Ramberg's place at six in the morning, and they'd go run at the track, doing sprints for an hour. Then after work Trent would go down to Chris's basement and they'd jump rope, do squats, burpees, and weights. Chris would tell Trent what he thought he needed to eat every day, and Trent would go home, have his meal, pass out exhausted, and get up the next morning to do it all over again, six days a week, pretty much all summer long.

This was a big change for Trent—he had hardly ever touched a weight until that summer. For a twenty-five-year-old pro hockey player, that was unheard of.

Chapter Thirty-One

While Trent was working out with Chris Ramberg, I got back on the phone and started calling all the NHL teams, telling them they had to look at Trent, touting his new resume that included eighteen points with the K-Wings the previous season.

I started checking out NHL prospect camps and tournaments. All this was pretty new to me at the time, but I researched online nonstop until I got a handle on things. I got many similar responses to what I had gotten when calling the minor league teams. "He was playing recreational hockey, what, are you nuts?" but I was persistent.

Finally I got a guy on the phone who seemed like he could help us out. Victor Saljanin was the head of scouting for the New York Rangers—another guy who might be able to suss out a diamond in the rough like Trent. Victor Saljanin was well connected to Glen Sather, the president and at that time general manager of the New York Rangers. Glen Sather was one of the great architects in the history of hockey management. Even the great Wayne Gretzky called Sather his mentor. I knew if I could get Trent in with Glen Sather, we'd be all set. So I got Victor Saljanin on the phone and said, "Victor, I've got a player I'm working with who I know Glen Sather is going to want to take a look at."

"Oh really, and who the heck are you?" asked Victor.

"My name is Jay Storm, and I'm working with one of the most overlooked players in the history of hockey, Trent Daavettila."

"Well, I've never heard of any Trent Daavettila," said Victor.

"You'd better get ready to hear a lot about him," I said. "He's a late-blooming Finlander, and he was playing in the men's leagues, but he shot right up to the IHL last season, and . . ."

"The men's leagues!" Victor said, interrupting me. "You do realize you're talking to the New York Rangers of the NHL, don't you, Jay?"

"You'd better believe I know who I'm talking to, Victor. I'm calling you guys because I've got an NHL-caliber player here, and you guys have to take a look at him. He scored eighteen points in twenty games with the Kalamazoo Wings last season, and he's just about guaranteed to skyrocket to the NHL next season, on to whichever team is lucky enough to get to him first."

"Jeez, Jay, you're really fired up about this guy," said Victor.

"Darn right I am. That's because he's one of the best young players out there, just you wait and see."

"I'll tell you what," said Victor. "I can't give you Glen Sather's phone number, but I can give you his secretary's email address. If you can carry the same excitement through email as you do on the phone, then maybe Glen will give you a call back."

So I wrote a long email to Glen Sather, telling him all about Trent, that he was an overlooked, late-blooming player who scored eighteen points in twenty games last season, without even being in shape. I told him about his unique vision and the eyes in the back of his head, as well as his stick-handling ability. I described in detail some of the goals he scored, and the assists he made with the K-Wings. I told him about his eleven siblings, Michigan Tech cutting him, and Pete South being a total jerk. And then I told him that we'd pay for everything if he'd let us go to the Rangers development camp. Heck, we'd camp out in New York and eat peanut butter slammers in the tent every night if it meant somebody with the Rangers would look at Trent.

A couple days later I got a call from Victor Saljanin. "Jay, Glen got your email," said Victor. "He was impressed, and you've got our ear. Can you tell me a little more about Trent?"

I told Victor everything I had written in the email to Glen, and more. "Listen," I said, "just get me on the phone with Glen Sather. I don't care how famous he is, I'll convince him that he needs to get Trent in the Rangers' training camp. I'll pay for everything—there's no risk to you guys. Just give us a chance; you won't regret it."

"Jay, hold on a minute. I'll call you back," said Victor.

Two hours later Victor called me back and said, "Jay, you're dealing with the New York Rangers."

"I know," I said.

"Glen is very impressed from what he's heard so far. We're going to invite Trent to our prospects camp that starts in three weeks."

"Awesome, man. Thank you!"

"Now slow down, because Trent's a little bit older than our typical training camp participant. We usually only invite college- and high school–aged kids to our development camp. But we're impressed so far, so we're making an exception."

"That's the right move, Victor," I said. "I know on paper Trent looks old, but he has no wear and tear."

"How do you mean, Jay?"

"Let me explain something to you," I said. "If you bought a brand new car and then parked it in a garage for eight years without ever driving it, it's still a brand new car with 250,000 miles left in it, right?"

"That seems right," said Victor, chuckling at my analogy.

"Well, that's what we're dealing with in regards to Trent Daavettila. He's like a Maserati that hasn't been driven in eight years," I said. "He's twenty-five years old, but he's had no wear and tear, so he's got the body of a kid fresh out of high school. So forget his freaking age. You've got yourself a brand new Maserati sitting in the garage that just needs a tune-up, which is exactly what he's doing right now with his personal trainer."

"Okay, Jay, we're excited to be working with you. I'll send you the itinerary for your trip to New York. And don't worry about your tent; you can leave that in the garage," said Victor, chuckling again. "We're going to set Trent up in a five-star hotel."

"That sounds great, Victor," I said. "Thanks a million. You won't be disappointed."

I got off the phone with Victor and called up Trent. "Trent, guess what?" I said. "You're going to the New York Rangers prospects camp, baby!"

"What? How the heck did you pull that off, Jay?"

"I don't know, but I did, so you're going. Congratulations."

"Wow, Jay, that's incredible!"

"You know you deserve it," I said. "The Rangers are going to be emailing us your itinerary. They're going to pay for your plane and hotel and everything."

"Heck yeah! What do I have to do?"

"I don't know much about these camps," I said. "All I know is that you've got to be in good shape."

"Well, I've been training six days a week with Chris, and I had a good twenty games last season, so I feel like I'm in the best shape of my life. When's the camp start?"

"It starts in three weeks. Just keep training every day, and get ready to go."

"Sounds good, Jay."

Chapter Thrity-Two

The development camp was a big deal. This was a camp that was largely attended by the top draft picks right out of college or the top prospects in the minor leagues. Inviting a player who had never played Division I college hockey, with only twenty games in the minors, was practically unimaginable. But there was Trent, with his ticket to New York City to go skate at Madison Square Garden.

I called Trent after he'd been in New York for a day and a half.

"Jay, it's amazing. There are so many good players here, and the facilities are awesome. It's hard as heck, though."

"Oh yeah, buddy. They tiring you out?"

"Heck yeah, they are. Their coach, John Tortorella, he's insane. He near about kills us every day. All the players are feeling it. Everyone is saying Tortorella is nuts. Tortorella isn't on the ice, but it's his program."

"That's all right, buddy. Just get some rest and stick with it. It'll be over in a couple days," I said.

I called Trent again on the fourth day of camp, and I could hear something was not right.

"What's going on, Trent? How you feeling?" I asked.

"Oh, not too good, Jay."

"How's that, buddy?"

"Oh jeez, Jay, I feel weird. I've never felt like this before in my life."

"You pretty sore then?"

"It's more than just sore, Jay. I was actually on my way to the hospital because I felt like I was dying."

"Well, don't die!"

"I'm okay now. I ran into the Rangers' trainers in the elevator, and they brought me back to my room. I've been eating noodles, and I'm slowly starting to come back to normal. Jeez, Jay. I thought I was in good shape, but not good enough for this camp apparently."

"Well, that's good you're eating. Keep eating!"

"Jay, I could only eat one noodle about every fifteen minutes because my body felt so weird. Everything was tingling. I felt like I was floating. The trainers are saying I'll be all right after I get some rest. But I was scared for a minute there."

"Well, jeez. Get some good sleep tonight and we'll see how you feel in the morning."

"All right, Jay. I'm sorry I let you down."

"You didn't let anyone down. You're doing great. And after only three weeks with Chris Ramberg. Hang in there. You're going to be all right."

The next day I called up Trent again. "Jay," he said, "I'm done. They wouldn't let me skate today because I'm just physically exhausted—way beyond what I'm used to."

"I hear you."

"Yeah, I'm a little embarrassed. I just wasn't up to handling that kind of rigorous training. My body wasn't ready for that."

"Don't worry about it. You're getting in better shape as we speak. How'd you do otherwise, though?"

"They seem to like me, Jay. I made a few assists and scored a goal. The coach of the Greenville Swamp Rabbits said he was interested in signing me."

"Way to be, buddy! Of course someone is interested in signing you. But don't sign anything yet. Nick Bootland in Kalamazoo is still interested in signing you. Let's get you back to Michigan, then we'll start working out a deal."

Chapter Thirty-Three

As Trent was traveling back from the prospects camp in New York, I called up Nick Bootland in Kalamazoo.

"Nick, it's Jay Storm. I wanted to give you an update on Trent Daavettila."

"Good to hear from you, Jay. How've you men been spending the summer?"

"Well, Trent has been at the New York Rangers prospect camp this past week."

"Are you serious, the New York Rangers prospect camp? They only let the top players in the country into those camps," said a surprised Bootland.

"Heck yeah, Nick. The New York Rangers invited Trent to their prospect camp. I told you Trent was good."

"That's pretty impressive."

"I know. So, here's the deal, Nick. We've got a few teams looking at Trent now. But I wanted to give you a call first, seeing as the K-Wings were the first team to ever give him a real shot. You ready to work out a deal?"

"Well," said Nick, holding back a bit, "I'm not so sure. You see, the K-Wings are moving up to the ECHL this year, and although Trent is an exceptional hockey player, I'm not sure he's good enough for the ECHL."

"That's fine, Nick, because another team in the ECHL is interested in Trent, the Greenville Swamp Rabbits, so I'll just give them a call." "Hold on a second," said Nick. "I don't think Trent should go to South Carolina."

"Oh, you don't? Why's that, Nick?"

"I think he was doing pretty good in Kalamazoo. I think it'd be better for his development if he stayed closer to home." I could tell Bootland was beating around the bush.

"Bootland, listen, if you want Trent on your team, you've got to say so. Because if he's not playing in Kalamazoo, we've got to sign him somewhere else."

"Okay, Jay. You sure do drive a hard bargain. Listen, get Trent in the best shape of his life, and we'll sign him for a season."

"Don't you worry about a thing, Nick. Wait till you see this kid next fall. You're going to have an NHL-caliber center-forward on your team. Trust me."

Meanwhile, Trent landed back in Michigan and called me a week later. "How you feeling, Trent?" I asked.

"I feel really good, Jay. Like a million bucks compared to last week, that's for sure. I'm ready to get back to it again."

"That's what I like to hear. Call Chris Ramberg up and get back in that gym."

Trent went back to work with Chris. They trained six days a week, all summer long. Meanwhile Trent was eating steaks, protein shakes, and pasta—whatever meal Ramberg suggested. And the results were starting to show. After not seeing him for a couple weeks, I exclaimed, "Who is this guy? You look like a pro hockey player all of a sudden!" I called Bootland again a few weeks before the season was set to start. "Wait till you see Trent," I said. "He's been working out all summer and has put on a lot of weight. He's going to be lights-out for you guys this season."

"I'm excited to take a look at him, Jay. But we've got a lot of good guys signed this year. Have you seen some of the guys on our roster so far?"

"Yeah, I've been looking," I said. Bootland had signed a bunch of young guys from big-name NCAA schools, some from the IHL, and a bunch from K-Wings–affiliated teams in New Jersey and Philadelphia. The K-Wings were pretty stacked, I had to admit.

"I don't know if Trent's going to fit in with all these big names around. We'll have to see how he does in tryouts," said Bootland.

"I wouldn't worry about that, Nick. Trent's going to be great for you guys—I guarantee you that Trent is going to be your best player."

Chapter Thirty-Four

As the summer came to a close, I called up Chris Ramberg. "How's it going with Trent?"

"Jay, I've had a great time working with Trent. He's incredibly dedicated. He's got a great attitude, does everything I tell him to do, never misses workouts, and we're seeing some pretty good results."

I met up with Trent a week before tryouts. "Holy cow, you look totally different!"

"Yeah, I know. Ramberg's really doing a good job. I feel super strong and ready for a full season."

"That's what I like to hear, bud. This is going to be your year. You're going to go into the ECHL and light that league up like a Christmas tree."

Even though the K-Wings tryouts were supposed to be closed to the public, I talked Nick Bootland into letting me watch.

I went down to Kalamazoo for the tryouts. After doing some drills on the ice, the whistles blew, and the guys got set for their first scrimmage.

Only five minutes into the scrimmage, Trent set up a goal. Five minutes later, he set up another goal. By the time the scrimmage was over, Trent had a goal and three assists, and his team won five to three.

I called Bootland after the scrimmage. "Nick," I said "you still got any doubt about Trent? He looks like the best kid on the ice to me."

"He looks good, Jay."

"You bet he does, Nick."

The next day, and for the rest of the camp, Trent stood out as one of the best players on the ice. At the end of the camp, they posted the roster on the team bulletin board, and there was Trent's name. His first full season as a pro hockey player was just a few weeks away.

Chapter Thirty-Five

Trent started out that season with the K-Wings as the second line center. The team was undergoing a ton of changes because of the big move over from the International Hockey League into the East Coast Hockey League. Things were different in the ECHL. For starters, the IHL had a total of six teams—all from the Midwest region—whereas the ECHL at that point had a total of twenty teams that spanned the entirety of the United States, from New Jersey to Alaska. And more importantly, the ECHL and the AHL were the only two minor hockey leagues recognized by the collective bargaining agreement between the National Hockey League and the National Hockey League Players' Association, meaning any player signed to an entry-level NHL contract and designated for assignment must report to a club in either the ECHL or the AHL. Trent was going to be playing with NHL-caliber players and getting looks from scouts affiliated with the biggest hockey teams in the western hemisphere.

K-Wings coach Nick Bootland wound up starting Trent as the second line center for the first four games. The K-Wings shot out of the start of the season like a rocket, winning their first four games, with Trent as one of the top scorers on the team. A few games after the season started, Bootland moved him up to the first line, and sure enough, Trent did even better. By twenty games into the season, Trent already had nine goals and nine assists, averaging nearly a point per game. He was doing everything I had expected him to do, and what no else could believe he would be able to at the ECHL level. And this was how it would go for essentially the rest of his career—every coach would at first doubt that Trent deserved to be playing on the first line, until they actually played him there, and then Trent would inevitably be the leader of the team. Every team he went to, in any league, Trent was able to become one of the top players if he was only given the chance to play on the first or second line.

After twenty games into the season—and Trent scoring a total of eighteen points—I got a call from Nick Bootland that proved Trent was beyond good enough to be playing in the ECHL.

"Jay, you're not going to believe this," said Bootland.

"What's that, Nick?"

"The Adirondack Phantoms of the AHL want to call up Trent."

"That's beautiful, man. But I've got to say, Nick, it isn't hard for me to believe."

Nicked chuckled a bit and said, "I know it, Jay. The Phantoms management called me up and asked me who our best player was. And I told him straight out, it's Trent Daavettila, there's no denying it."

"Heck yeah, buddy. I appreciate your integrity," I told him.

"It's crazy, but you're right, Jay. I still hold my breath every time Trent gets out on the ice, thinking he's going to get killed. But nobody can hit this guy."

"Well yeah, Nick. Hitting Trent is like hitting a ghost. People think they can hit him, but no one ever does. He's always been like that."

"It's pretty cool he's taking his game up to the AHL now, isn't it?"

"Yeah, it's awesome. Can't say I'm surprised, though. I'm telling you, there's no ceiling on this kid's career."

Well the truth is, I wasn't surprised Trent got the call up, but I was super excited. The Adirondack Phantoms were a farm team for the Philadelphia Flyers, so that meant Trent was going to be playing with players who had already seen ice time with NHL teams that season. And to think that just the previous year he was still out of shape, working a structural engineering job, with everyone in the IHL giving him the cold shoulder. The call up from the Phantoms made it feel like every step we were taking was a step in the right direction.

Chapter Thirty-Six

Trent flew over to Glen Falls, New York, where the Adirondack Phantoms played. Glen Falls is a tiny city of fifteen thousand in way upstate New York—closer to the Vermont and Canadian borders than it is to New York City. It's less than one quarter the size of Kalamazoo—but like Kalamazoo, it has a strong hockey history. The Detroit Red Wings–affiliated Adirondack Red Wings played there for twenty years, beginning in 1979. That's when the Glen Falls Civic Center was built, in 1979. The civic center is a midsize hockey arena—around five thousand seats—that somehow manages to sell out on regular basis. Although the Adirondack Red Wings folded in 1999, AHL-affiliated teams have played in the Glen Falls Civic Center almost every year since. Somehow, they manage to sell out a stadium that is one-third the size of the town it resides in. That just goes to show you the strength of the hockey culture in upstate New York.

The Phantoms set Trent up in a hotel in Glen Falls. We had no idea how long he would be there or where he would be going next, but from then until he was told otherwise, Trent was going to be based out of Glen Falls, NY, and traveling wherever the Phantoms traveled.

The Phantoms were off to a pretty lousy start that season, at the bottom of the AHL Eastern division. That didn't stop Trent from trying to get a leg-up in the AHL, however. The Flyers' scouts were all over that team, so all we needed was the chance for Trent to show them what he was made of.

Unfortunately that chance never really came for Trent. You see, when they call guys up to a new team, they often put them on the fourth line—at least at first. And the Phantoms weren't set up for Trent's kind of talent. They put him on the fourth line with two fighters named Garrett Klotz and Matt Clackson. In pro hockey, what we call a fighter is a big, heavy guy who only serves one real purpose—to crush guys into the boards and then beat the crap out of them. It seemed like Clackson and Klotz could only skate in a straight line and that they'd rather hit a guy than try to make a play.

Of course, Trent didn't much care about hitting guys. In fact, he was essentially the antithesis of this type of player. He was the ghost who no one could hit—the guy with eyes in the back of his head, who had the ability to put the puck in between defenders, to set up scoring chances, or get the shot on net himself. If Trent was going to show the scouts his true talents, he was going to need to get on a line with some other guys who wanted to score, not a couple of bruisers looking for a fight.

On his first shift playing in the AHL against the Hershey Bears, Trent stripped the puck from a defender and went in on a breakaway. He probably would have scored, too, if a goalie named Michal Neuvirth hadn't robbed him.

After ten games with the Phantoms, they finally put Trent on the power play, which was obviously going to be a good chance to show the coaches what he was worth. And sure enough, as soon as he got on the ice he set up a backdoor tap-in goal. The guy he set up for a goal, Jason Ward, said afterward, "I haven't had a pass like that in ten years." Trent wound up getting two assists that day, and the Phantoms went on to win the game.

Trent called me up after the game and said, "Jay, I finally got some power play minutes."

"Oh yeah, how did you do?"

"Well, I had two assists, and we went on to win the game."

"Well, that sure doesn't surprise me!"

"I figured you'd say something like that, Jay. Anyway, I imagine now that I've scored a couple of points the coach will be more confident to play me more."

"If he knows what's good for him, he will!" I said.

Unfortunately it doesn't always go that way in the AHL. That league has hundreds of players, all looking for the same shot. And just because you do well on a couple power plays doesn't mean you're guaranteed to move up in the ranks. We were slowly beginning to find out that you didn't move up in professional hockey simply based on merit of play. The coaches and managers chose kids they had drafted or that were big-time college free agents. Trent didn't quite fit that typical profile of professional hockey player, and he often got overlooked despite his consistent high level of play.

The next game after Trent's chance on the power play, the other forwards had come back from their injuries, and the coach put Trent right back on the fourth line with the pair of heavyweights. Those two assists would be the only points Trent would score for the Adirondack Phantoms.

Trent played a total of thirteen games with the Phantoms that season. Unfortunately, Trent's stats for the Adirondacks don't make him look like any sort of superhero—two assists over thirteen games. It's telling that the Phantoms were at the bottom of their division that year. If Trent was going to get a good look from NHL scouts, he was going to need to get on a team with coaches that could recognize his talents and play him accordingly.

At that point I started to question my own abilities as an agent. It was clear that given the chance, Trent could keep up with AHL-caliber players, but he hadn't gotten a fair shake under my watch. I wanted so badly to help Trent reach that end goal of the NHL, but even more than helping him get there, I wanted to see him achieve his dreams, whether I could claim partial responsibility or not. I thought maybe it was time for me to step aside and let Trent work with somebody who had more experience with pro hockey. I called Trent to see how he felt about that.

"Trent, I've been thinking," I said to him over the phone, "that maybe you should start looking for another agent."

"Why? Is everything all right?" He sounded worried.

"Yeah, everything is fine. I just have been thinking maybe the reason you're not getting a fair shake at the AHL level is because people don't trust me. I mean, I've never worked as a pro hockey agent before—I think you might have a better shot if you were working with someone who had a little more experience and connections."

"Jay, what on earth are you talking about? I don't want another agent, man."

"Yeah, but are you sure you don't?"

"Of course I'm sure! I wouldn't be doing any of this if weren't for you. You're the one who keeps telling me not to quit until we reach the goal. If you're not doing that for me, then who is gonna do it?"

"Well, I thought maybe another agent . . ."

"Jay, listen to me—in no way do I want another agent. Either we make it together or we don't make it at all. So if you're thinking about quitting, I'm going to do it before you get the chance."

"Okay, Trent. Okay, I hear you. I ain't quitting, I just want you to have the best shot."

"You're the only shot, Jay."

"All right, then let's find that next tryout!"

Chapter Thirty-Seven

After a month in Glen Falls with the Phantoms, Trent was on his way back to Kalamazoo. We were learning quickly that playing pro hockey at the ECHL and AHL level was going to mean a lot of instability and moving around. Trent was OK with that, though—he was set up in an apartment in Kalamazoo with a K-Wings teammate at the time, and they were both all about hockey twenty-four hours a day.

Once back in Kalamazoo, Trent started lighting up the boards again. The K-Wings were doing extraordinarily well, considering it was their first season in the ECHL. They led the North Division for the majority of the season. And despite his twenty-game absence while with the Phantoms, Trent was still the fourth-best scorer on the team.

Meanwhile, I was calling teams all over the AHL, looking for someone who'd be willing to give Trent some time on the ice. Unfortunately, Trent's stat sheet with Adirondack was so lousy, I could hardly get anybody on the phone, let alone someone to listen to me go on about why Trent deserved a chance on the first line of their team. I'd try to explain that Trent's stats didn't look good on paper, but in reality he hadn't had a chance on the ice. As soon as he was on the power play, he had two points. All the other games he was playing three shifts a period, on a line with a couple of fighters who could only skate in a straight line and smash guys into the boards. If you were to add up all of Trent's shifts over those thirteen games, he probably had fewer shifts than in the one game where he made two assists!

It was a tough sell with a lot of competition, but we did wind up getting one more call-up to the AHL that season—this time with the Grand Rapids Griffins. Of course, general manager Bob McNamara had already gotten a good look at Trent the previous season, when he practiced with the Griffins at Joe Louis Arena, so Trent did end up getting a little more ice time with them than he did with the Phantoms. And despite scoring a goal during his first game he played with them, the Griffins decided it wasn't the year to be signing Trent to a contract, so they sent him back down to the K-Wings after only two games.

Luckily Trent wasn't slowing down at all with the K-Wings. That year Trent led the team into the Kelly Cup playoffs. The Kelly Cup is the ECHL version of the Stanley Cup, featuring eight teams with the best records from across the country competing for the championship. The K-Wings won the North Division that year and got the second seed in their conference, but then lost the five-game series against a surprisingly good Reading Royals team in the first round. In the five playoff games that the K-Wings played, Trent scored three goals and two assists—five points total over five games. Not bad for his first time in an ECHL playoff tournament. We thought we had a pretty good stat sheet to work with going into the offseason trying to get an AHL or NHL contract for Trent.

Chapter Thirty-Eight

After that first full season with Kalamazoo was over, I kept working the phones. I called every team in the AHL, but most of the time I couldn't even get anyone to talk to me, let alone consider letting Trent go in for a tryout. At the ECHL the best way to get called up was to be recognized by a coach, like the way Nick Bootland had told the Phantoms that Trent was the best player on the K-Wings, or of course to be a drafted player or a free agent straight out of a good college career, which, thanks to the coaches who had passed him over at Michigan Tech, Trent would never be.

While I was working the phones, Trent was training again with Chris Ramberg. He spent that summer working as hard as he could, thinking that with the success he had had the previous year, he was sure to be getting some looks from the AHL teams.

Another big event in Trent's life occurred that summer. That was the year he married his wife, Wendy. He had met Wendy in Minnesota a few years prior. In many ways Wendy's a lot like Trent, and was a hockey player as well—she had played in high school back in Minnesota.

Married life changed Trent a bit—for instance, he wasn't eating takeout pizza every night, and his apartment started looking a little nicer than it did when he had lived with his buddy. But married life didn't alter his productivity on the hockey rink. Despite the grind of the ECHL season, Wendy supported Trent's constant traveling and night games. We all thought Trent's pursuit of his hockey dreams was worthwhile as long as there remained a chance of him playing in the NHL. If he could just get on a big-league team, then all of the other pieces would surely fall into place.

Trent kept working hard, and when the next season came around, he was in better shape than ever. And it paid off. The K-Wings picked up right where they had left off the year before as one of the top scoring teams in the league, and a key part of that scoring success was Trent's ability to make plays.

Trent got one look at the AHL level that season when Bob McNamara and the Grand Rapids Griffins called him to replace an injured forward. Unfortunately the same thing happened with the Griffins that season that had happened with the Phantoms the season before—Trent played about three shifts a period on the fourth line. The coach sent him out there to flip the puck down ice and go hit guys, which was definitely not Trent's game.

I called up Bob McNamara after the game to see why the Griffins were holding Trent back.

"Bob, it's great you called up Trent for another game with the Griffins, but why are you playing him on the fourth line with those bruisers? Those guys don't play Trent's game. Trent's a playmaker, not a fighter."

"Hey, Jay, yeah, unfortunately we got orders from Joe Louis Arena to play our draft picks at the moment. We simply don't have a spot for a guy like Trent right now," said McNamara.

"Don't have a spot—well, what the heck did you call him up for then?"

"We had some guys get hurt and we needed a spot start from a forward who can play. We know Trent's the best player on the K-Wings roster at the moment, so he was the guy we called."

"Well, if he's the best player on the K-Wings, don't you think he could be a great player on the Griffins? You guys aren't exactly lights-out this season—it seems like you could use a guy who knows how to score some points," I said.

"I hear you, Jay. But unfortunately I'm powerless in this situation. The orders come from Detroit, and I have to follow them."

"That's baloney," I said and hung up the phone.

That phone call frustrated the life right out of me. If Trent was playing so good with the K-Wings, why the heck couldn't he get a look at the AHL level?

Back in Kalamazoo with coach Nick Bootland, however, Trent was looking like a superstar. He wound up being the second-leading scorer in the ECHL that season, with eighty points over just seventy-one games—averaging over one point a game. Trent's scoring led the K-Wings to the Kelly Cup playoffs for the second year in row.

The K-Wings were the third seed that year, behind the Greenville Road Warriors and the Reading Royals. They breezed through the first round and then swept the Royals four games to none in the second round.

Trent lit up the scoreboards left and right, and led the team all the way to the Kelly Cup finals against the Alaska Aces. That was a fun series, because the K-Wings got to travel up to Anchorage, Alaska, for a few games—the farthest away that they could travel from Kalamazoo for an ECHL game. The K-Wings ended up losing to the Aces in five games, but Trent was the leading scorer in the entire playoffs that year, and he was also recognized with the Rebook Plus Performer of the Year award.

Chapter Thirty-Nine

That summer between Trent's second and third season with the K-Wings, I got a call from the general manager of the St. John's IceCaps, Craig Heisinger. The IceCaps were a Winnipeg Jets–affiliated AHL team, located in St. Johns, Newfoundland. Heisinger called me up out of the blue a few days after the K-Wings season had ended.

"Jay, I'm calling because we're looking for another high-scoring center forward in our organization, and our scouts are saying we should invite your guy Trent Daavettila to our tryouts next fall."

"Well, you're darn right you should. If you're looking for a high-scoring forward, Trent's your guy," I said.

"Great, so come on out to Halifax next September and we'll see if Trent is a good fit for the IceCaps."

"Sounds good! I'll let Trent know," I said and hung up the phone.

Boy, it was about time to get this sort of news! Finally an AHL team was going to get a solid look at Trent. This would be the perfect level for him to step in and show management that he belonged in the AHL.

I called Trent up to let him know the good news. "Holy cow, Jay! How'd you pull that off?" Trent said, being his typical humble self.

"It wasn't me. They called me out of the blue. They probably had scouts at one of your K-Wing games or something along those lines.

But you think you want to do it? You'll be going all the way to Nova Scotia, Canada, and then if you get signed, I imagine you'll have to move there."

"Jay, of course I want to do it! To tell you the truth, it sounds like the perfect thing for me. At this point, I'd do almost anything to get on an AHL team."

"That's what I like to hear. You don't have to do anything different than what you've been doing. Just keep training with Chris Ramberg, and get set to go to Cleveland on September 17th."

"Sounds good, Jay!"

Trent went to work training with Chris Ramberg, and I focused on my other business that summer rather than trying to land a new AHL contract, because I was satisfied with the prospects of Trent attending the IceCaps training camp in the fall.

Meanwhile, Trent announced another huge occurrence in his personal life—the upcoming arrival of his first child, who was to be born in September, right before the season began. Everyone was super happy for Trent and his wife Wendy.

Everything was going along perfectly. Trent was working hard, getting in excellent shape, and Wendy was a healthy and happy mother-to-be. She was scheduled to have the baby the third week in September, and Trent was scheduled to leave on the twenty-seventh for the ten-day camp in Nova Scotia, some fifteen hundred miles away.

Two days before the camp started I got a call from Trent. "Jay, I've got some bad news."

"What's that?"

"I can't go to the camp," said Trent flat out.

"What? Oh no, you've got to be kidding me. Why the heck not?"

"It's my son Conner, Jay. He came a week early, and he's been sick."

"Sick?"

"Yeah, he had fluid in his lungs when he was born. He was having trouble breathing, wheezing a lot—it was super scary, Jay. I thought he might not make it—and then they eventually found the problem—a hole in one of his lungs."

"Jeez, Trent. I'm sorry to hear that. Is he all right?"

"They incubated him and put a chest tube in his lungs. After five days, he took a turn for the good, and everything is okay now."

"Thank goodness!"

"I know. Jay, I feel super bad missing the training camp, but I've got to stay at home with Wendy and Conner until everything is settled. We had quite a scare. Neither of us have slept in over a week. To tell you the truth, I'm so exhausted I don't even think I could lace up my skates right now."

"Don't worry about the training camp. There will be other training camps. Just stay focused on your family, and you've got the K-Wings season starting up in about a month. Hang tight and take care of your family, Trent."

"Okay, Jay. I'm glad you understand."

"Trent, of course I understand. You know I've got kids of my own, right? First thing you learn when you have a kid is that being a dad comes before all else."

"Yes, I can totally see how that's true after this last week," Trent said, chuckling a bit.

"Darn right. I imagine you can. Oh, and one more thing, Trent."

"What's that, Jay?"

"Congratulations on becoming a father."

"Thanks, Jay. I appreciate everything you've done for me, as usual. It means a lot right now."

I'd be lying if I said I wasn't disappointed that Trent wasn't going to the IceCaps training camp. Looking back, it's easy to imagine how that training camp might have changed both of our lives. If Trent got signed, he and Wendy would have moved to Newfoundland, and most likely he would have been lights out at St. Johns, just like he had been everywhere else. Then what? Getting signed with the Winnipeg Jets would have been the next obvious step. I was disappointed that he wasn't playing with an AHL or NHL team, but in another sense, I was glad I could still watch him play in Kalamazoo on a regular basis. Plus the community was super supportive of his new life as a hockey dad. Both Wendy's and Trent's families were close by to help babysit, and the reporter for the local newspaper even did a nice write-up about Trent being a hockey dad.

So Trent and his young family stayed in Kalamazoo. His third season with the K-Wings went almost as well as his previous two. He was one of the top scorers in the ECHL for the third year in a row, and he had the most points of any player on the K-Wings.

At the same time as being a full-time hockey player, Trent was spending a lot of time with Conner. The hockey schedule fit being a new dad perfectly—Trent would go into practice at nine in the morning, be done by one in the afternoon, then he'd run straight home to help Wendy with feeding their son and changing diapers.

Trent eventually did make it to Nova Scotia that season, when the IceCaps called him up for a couple games. But those two games went pretty much like his stints with the Grand Rapids Griffins and the Adirondack Phantoms—he played well, but you wouldn't know it from the stat sheet because he only got three or four shifts each game. It's a shame, because clearly someone in the IceCaps system had their eye on Trent, but things weren't lining up perfectly for him to have a chance to be a full-time player for their team. Just another unlucky break that could have easily gone the other way had the timing been better.

The K-Wings went on to the Kelly Cup playoffs for the third season in a row that year. They wound up losing in the conference finals to the Florida Everblades, but Trent was yet again the top scorer on the team.

As the season was coming to an end, I thought I'd bark up the tree of a few European pro hockey teams. I started talking with several teams in leagues on the other side of the Atlantic who were on the lookout for new talent. Eventually I connected with a team in Denmark called the Frederikshavn White Hawks. They were ready to fly Trent out there for the season. Playing in Denmark would mean more exposure in a whole new market. Although I liked Trent playing in Michigan so I could go watch him, I was pretty pumped on the idea of him going to Europe. So I got the deal all set up, and Trent was talking over the big move to Denmark with Wendy. Then one day after the K-Wings season was over, I got a call from Trent.

"Jay, I think I'm done," he said out of the blue.

"Done with what?" I replied.

"I think I'm done playing hockey, Jay."

"What on earth are you talking about? You just had another great season. You're one of the top scorers in the league, and I'm working on several deals right now."

"Yeah I know, Jay. But Wendy's pregnant with our second child, so I'm thinking about getting a steady engineering job now."

"I understand the desire to start your engineering career, Trent. But you're in your prime right now. I just got this deal in Europe, and who knows where that could take you," I said.

"I know. I've been talking it over with Wendy, and to tell you the truth, we're both a little nervous about going to Denmark right about the time when we're supposed to give birth to our second child. And also my only goal when I started this journey was to make it to the NHL, and if I go to Europe I'm basically giving up that dream, and I don't want to do that. I want to keep grinding over here in the States, and hope eventually I get a chance to prove myself at the next level."

"I hear you. That makes sense."

"Sorry, Jay. I really appreciate you pushing me all these years. I wish we had made it to that next level. But at the same time, I'm grateful for getting as far as we did."

"I understand, Trent. I wish you had gotten there too. I know you're good enough to be playing in the NHL."

"Ah, jeez, Jay. It's nice to hear you say that. But I'm not so sure it's true."

"Trent, don't sell yourself short." Then I got an idea that likely saved Trent's hockey career. "I tell you what. I understand you're getting ready to settle down. But what if you could play for another team in the ECHL? Get a change of scenery, see a different part of the country before settling down for good."

"Well, we have talked about getting out of Michigan. But where are you thinking, Jay?"

"You tell me, Trent. Where would you like to go if you could play for any team in the ECHL?"

"Well, to tell the truth, Wendy and I have sort of been talking about how cool it would be to live in Colorado—I've always loved Colorado."

"Trent, don't quit yet. If you really want to go to Colorado, there may be more hockey in your future yet. You'll be hearing from me soon," I said and hung up the phone.

Chapter Forty

If Trent wanted to go to Colorado, that would mean I'd have to get him a contract with the only ECHL team in that state—the Colorado Eagles. The Eagles had moved to the ECHL from the Central Hockey League the previous season, so there was a good chance that they were looking for ECHL–caliber players. It was definitely worth a shot, and given that Trent was going to retire unless he could move his family to Colorado, it was the only shot I had at extending his pro hockey career.

Trent was still under contract with Kalamazoo, so he wouldn't be able to play anywhere else in the ECHL unless he was traded or the K-Wings agreed to release him. Since Trent had little chance of getting traded, considering he was one of the most valuable players in the league at that point and had become somewhat of a local hero in Kalamazoo, before I could call up the Eagles to talk about a deal, I'd have to talk to Nick Bootland at the K-Wings to see if they'd be willing to release Trent.

This was a tough call, because I didn't want to disappoint Bootland. Out of all the coaches and managers we had worked with, Nick had perhaps done the most for us. He stuck his neck out for Trent when nobody else would, and for that I was going to be forever grateful. I didn't feel all that good about telling him that his star player wanted to go to another team, but at that point we had no other option.

"Nick," I said, "bad news. Trent's talking about retirement."

"What? No way. You've got to be pulling my leg. Trent's in the prime of his career, and he has been our best player for the past three seasons!"

"I'm not pulling your leg, Nick. I just talked to him a few hours ago. In case you haven't heard, Trent and his wife are about to have their second kid."

"Well, I'm happy for him, Jay. But I've got to say, I think it's a shame that he doesn't want to play hockey anymore. He's been our leading scorer for the past three seasons."

"I know, I know. I think it's a shame too. Believe me, there's nothing more than I want for Trent but for him to keep playing hockey. But listen, Nick. The thing is, Trent and his wife would really like to move out of Michigan, and he might play another season if I could get him on a different team someplace else."

"Jeez, Jay. A different team. I don't know if I like the sound of that!" said Nick.

"I know, Nick. Can't say I love it either. But if he doesn't go play somewhere else, he's going to retire anyway. So I gotta ask—would the K-Wings be willing to release Trent?"

"Oh come on, Jay!" Bootland said, sounding angry and surprised.

"Nick, I can tell you don't want to let him go, and believe me, I understand why. But there's no other option for Trent. He's got his mind set on his family, and they want out of Michigan, at least for a little while."

"Okay, Jay. If the deal is that he's going to retire anyway, I'd rather see him play somewhere else than not at all, so I guess we've got to let him go," said Nick, sounding dejected.

"Thanks for understanding, Nick."

I hung up the phone with Bootland and immediately began to think about my next phone call—a call to the Colorado Eagles.

Chapter Forty-One

The Colorado Eagles were based in the city of Loveland, Colorado. They had joined the league just the year before Trent decided he wanted to make the move and had made the playoffs their first year in the league. It seemed like a good spot for Trent to go. He'd have a chance to play in front of scouts and fans that had never seen him play on a regular basis before—perhaps increasing his chances with a new AHL team, and Loveland seemed like a town both he and Wendy could appreciate.

So I called up Chris Stewart, the coach of the Eagles, and said, "Hey Chris, what would you say if I told you I'm the agent for the best player in the ECHL, and that player wants to come play for you?"

"Well, I guess the first thing I'd say is what player is that you're talking about?" replied Chris.

"Trent Daavettila."

"Who?"

You have got to be kidding me? I thought. *This guy doesn't know who Trent is?* Now I knew for sure he was new to the ECHL. "Trent Daavettila, the first-line center for the K-Wings," I said.

"I don't know much about him, Jay," said Chris.

"Well, look him up, buddy. I think you'll be impressed."

"All right. We are looking for some new talent, so I'll check him out and give you a call back," Chris said and hung up the phone.

Five minutes later Chris called me back. "That kid wants to come play for the Eagles?" he said as soon as I picked up the phone.

"That's right. He told me if he could play anywhere, he'd like to play in Colorado."

"But isn't he under contract with the K-Wings?" asked Chris.

"He was, until two days ago when he told me he wanted to move to Colorado. I just got him released right before I called you."

"Well, why does he want to come out here, Jay? It seems like he's doing all right in Kalamazoo."

"Trent's a family man now, Chris. He and his wife, Wendy, are about to have their second child, and they want a change of scenery. He told me they want to go to Colorado."

"Well, if Trent wants to move to Colorado, that sounds pretty darn good for the Eagles! In fact, I really want him to come play for us. We could use an upgrade at center. Tell you what, why doesn't Trent and his family fly out here? I can show them around Loveland, and we can talk things over. If everything goes well, we can write up a contract."

"That sounds great, Chris. I'll let Trent know."

The next thing I did was call up Trent, to make sure he and Wendy were still into the idea of moving to a new state.

"Hey, how are things? How's the family?"

"Well, we're hanging in there, Jay. Wendy's three months pregnant. I'm still trying to figure out what life after hockey is going to be like, though. I'm still not used to the idea, to tell you the truth."

"Well, don't get too used to it at all, because remember how you told me you'd be willing to play next season if you could move to Colorado? Well, guess what? You've got a deal with the Colorado Eagles if you want one."

"Jay, are you serious? You're frickin' unbelievable."

"It's not set yet, of course. But Chris Stewart, the coach of the Colorado Eagles, has offered to fly you, Wendy, and Conner out to Loveland and show you around. If you like the place, we'll sign a deal and you can start the next season out there."

"Well jeez, Jay. I'll have to talk things over with Wendy, of course. But so far this sounds about like the ideal situation for us," Trent said and hung up the phone.

I arranged for Trent and his family to fly out to Colorado, and Chris put them up in a hotel and showed them around the city of Loveland for a couple days. Loveland is a small city of about 66,000 in the foothills of the Rocky Mountains, about fifty miles north of Denver. There are beautiful snow-capped mountains to the west and desert plains to the east, with lots of ski resorts and little lakes all around. And to accompany the beautiful scenery, the Eagles were running a top-notch ECHL operation. The Eagles had a fairly new stadium—the Budweiser Events Center—which sold out its 7,200 seats on a regular basis for their games. Trent and Wendy loved it out there, so Chris and I made up a contract, while the two of them got set up in a nice little house near the hockey stadium, and Trent got ready to start the coming hockey season with a new team.

Chapter Forty-Two

Maybe it was because he wasn't training with Chris Ramberg, or maybe because he was getting used to the new team, or maybe the new team was getting used to him, but whatever the reason, Trent didn't get off to the best start in Colorado. Coach Chris Stewart had never seen him play before—he had signed Trent based purely on his stat sheet and my word—so he started him on the third line—at left wing, no less—and Trent wasn't producing the way he had been in Kalamazoo. Five games into that first season in Colorado I got a voice mail from Chris.

"Hey, Jay," he said. "I'm not really sure what's going on. We've had Trent on for five games and he's not doing what we've been expecting him to. No points at all in any of these five games. We'd really like to see him start producing some points for us. Give me a call back and let me know what you think."

Boy, that sure got me. I had been watching the games on the Internet, and I knew exactly why Trent wasn't producing—Chris wasn't playing him to his talents. The other guys on the third line didn't play the game in the same way Trent did—they weren't as quick and couldn't handle his passes like top-line forwards were supposed to. Plus Trent had next to zero power play time up to that point. It was like the trouble we had with all the call-ups to the AHL all over again, but this time at the ECHL level. It was ridiculous guys were still treating Trent like that. It made me miss Nick Bootland in Kalamazoo.

To me it was clear as day that Trent should be starting every game. So I called up Chris Stewart and told him just that. I said, "Chris, I got your message, and it's pretty darn clear to me why Trent hasn't scored any points in his first five games."

"Why's that, Jay?" asked Chris.

"Because you're not playing him to his strengths!" I said, almost shouting with frustration. "You've got him out on the third line with a couple of public skaters who don't know how to play. And on top of that, he's had next to zero power play minutes so far. Now why the heck are you complaining, given this ridiculous situation you have him in?"

"Well jeez, Trent just got to Colorado, Jay. I wanted to see what he could do before starting him. And so far he hasn't done anything—not a single goal or an assist, and we've lost all but one game out of the first five this season."

"Listen, Chris, don't tell me Trent hasn't done anything. He's been one of the top scorers in the league for the past three seasons. You're treating him like a redheaded stepchild, just like every other new team he's joined in the past who failed to see the talent of this kid! You know how Trent became the lead scorer of the K-Wings, the recipient of the Reebok Plus Performer award, and has been one of the top scorers in the ECHL since he was a rookie four seasons ago?

Coach Nick Bootland recognized his talents and then played him accordingly. Now if you're not going to start him on the first line, you might as well trade him back to Kalamazoo!"

"Maybe we should trade him back then," said Chris.

"Go ahead and do that. Do that, and I guarantee you you'll be the laughingstock of the ECHL!" I hung up the phone in a fit of frustration. I had heard this kind of talk long enough from coaches and managers in both the ECHL and the AHL, and I sure as heck wasn't going to take it from Chris Stewart.

The next day Trent called me up and said, "Hey, guess what? I'm playing on the first line tonight!"

That sure made me chuckle. I guess my rant on the phone had gotten through to Chris. "That's great! That's where you should have been playing all along."

"Yeah, that's what I was expecting. I just can't seem to get going with these guys I've been playing with on the third line."

"I know, Trent. I've been watching the games online, and last night I had a conversation with your coach. I told him he should play you on the first line or consider trading you."

"Well, hopefully I can get something going, in that case. Because I sure as heck don't want to move now. We're just getting settled in out here, and Wendy's about to give birth any day now."

"Listen, don't worry about all of that. Just do what you know how to do on the ice, and everything else is going to fall into place."

When Trent got on the first line, it was like he was shot out of a cannon. He scored about twenty points in the next twelve games, and there was no looking back. He was starting every game, scoring a good portion of the Eagles' points, and once again led his team back to the Kelly Cup playoffs.

Trent was rewarded for his high level of play with another call-up to the AHL—this time with the Chicago Wolves. And like all the other AHL teams, they played him on the fourth line without any power play minutes, and only three or four shifts a period. I wasn't quite getting why these teams kept calling him up but never utilizing his natural talents. Even so, he still managed to get an assist in that one game with the Wolves, giving us reason to hold out hope for the next chance.

Chapter Forty-Three

After that first season in Colorado was over, I got another phone call from Chris Stewart, and boy had his tune changed from that voice mail I had received at the beginning of the season.

"Jay, I gotta say," said Chris, "you were right. Trent's a phenomenal hockey player."

"Heck yeah! Don't we know it," I said. "I've been watching online—you guys have had a pretty good season."

"True, not bad for our second season in the ECHL. But Jay, not only is Trent a phenomenal hockey player, he's also a great leader and an all-around good human being. That's why I've decided to make him team captain next season."

"That's what I like to hear, Chris! I think that will be a great role for Trent!" I had to say that Chris sure was doing a heck of a job coaching the Eagles. At that point he'd already been coaching pro hockey for twenty-five years, and as soon as he said he was making Trent captain, it was pretty clear that he knew a thing or two above some of the other guys in his position.

We were pumped that Trent got named the captain after only one season in Colorado, but I still had a feeling that other AHL or even

NHL teams would be interested in signing him, if only he could get back to an AHL training camp so one of the teams might get a good look at him. So I got back on the phones again and started calling every team in the AHL. And like before, I ran into the same sorts of obstacles that I had since I'd first started out as Trent's agent.

By this time a few more guys around the league already knew who Trent was and would express interest, but most of the time they'd say something like, "Just hold on until after the draft, Jay, and we'll see where we're at then. If we don't get a forward that can step onto the ice for us in the draft, maybe we'll take a look at Trent." Unbelievably, Trent still wasn't getting the respect he deserved because of not being drafted right out of college or at least having been an undrafted free agent with a Division I team. Well that just wasn't the way it went with Trent. Michigan Tech hadn't given him the proper chance, and then guys like Pete South with the Flint Generals had screwed us over, and even though those guys were all kicking themselves now for not recruiting one of the best undrafted professional hockey players of Trent's generation, it didn't matter. Trent just didn't have the resume most pro teams were used to seeing. Managers I would call would still say, "But he was playing in a men's league, Jay. We don't take players who come out of men's leagues." Men's leagues! That was five seasons ago! For some reason, being one of the top scorers in the ECHL wasn't good enough for the big time.

Jarrod Skalde, former head coach of the Bloomington Prairie Thunder, was one character on our radar as that season got started. Skalde had cut Trent earlier, but we had stayed in touch, and he always told me he regretted cutting him. As Skalde moved around coaching jobs in the IHL and the ECHL, he faced Trent many times, and of course wound up getting beaten by Trent on a regular basis. I would often talk to Skalde after those games, and he told me on a number of occasions that he wished he had signed Trent when he'd had the chance and that he deserved to be on an AHL team. In the year before Trent went to Colorado, I remember Skalde telling me that if he ever went on to coach an AHL team, he would try to bring Trent with him.

Well, as it turned out, Skalde had just gotten a new coaching job with the Norfolk Admirals of the AHL. So as the preseason was beginning that year, I thought I'd check in on Skalde's promise.

"Remember when you told me that if you ever went to the AHL, you'd take Trent with you?" I said to Skalde on the phone one afternoon. "You know how good he is, man. He's been beating up on your teams ever since you cut him."

"I know, Jay. I know Trent's good," said Skalde. "But I can't start bringing in new talent from the ECHL right now—I just got here and I feel like I'm walking on eggshells."

"Come on, Skalde. You're an assistant coach in the AHL—grow a pair, man! You won't be getting anywhere being a yes man. Stick your neck out for Trent. He's gonna make you look good—going to bat for a player of Trent's caliber and pulling him up from the ECHL will help your coaching career a bunch when all is said and done."

"Jay, I'm telling you, I can't be taking a gamble on a player like Trent right now. It's my first season in the AHL, and I've got to play it by the book."

"A gamble? What on this green earth are you referring to as a gamble? Listen, man, you and I both know that Trent ain't no gamble. You've watched him rocket past your teams for the last four years. Trent ain't a gamble—he's a sure thing to score against your team, unless you sign him. When playing against you, Trent's a liability, not a gamble!"

"Well, if that's the case, it's not my place to change that, Jay. At least not this season. I wish you guys the best, and I hope I get a chance to play against Trent in the AHL at some point soon. And if I do, you can be sure I'll be watching to see how he handles himself at the AHL level." And with that, Skalde hung up the phone, leaving me back at the drawing board.

I wasn't about to give up. Every time Trent had gotten a proper chance at a higher level, he was able to impress, so I kept looking for the next opportunity.

One AHL team that came pretty close to signing Trent that preseason was the Chicago Wolves. The Wolves were the team that had called Trent up the previous season, and even though he only had played ten shifts in a single game, they at least knew who he was and that he was capable of scoring points.

I got the Wolves General Manager, Wendell Young, on the phone. "Wendell, Jay Storm here," I said. "I want to talk to you about Trent Daavettila."

"Who are you calling about?" asked Wendell.

"Trent Daavettila. The center forward from the Colorado Eagles who scored a point in the three minutes you guys had him on the ice last season," I replied smugly.

"Oh, Trent Daavettila, of course, he's a good center. Kinda small, but a good center forward nonetheless. What can I do for you?"

"Well, that's just the thing, Wendell. You see, Trent's size isn't the issue. The issue is that Trent has been one of the top scorers in the ECHL for the last four seasons, and no one has played him more than a handful of minutes in any AHL game. Every chance he has on a line with some players that can keep up with him, he scores. Now why the heck isn't he getting any ice time at the AHL level? Don't you think it's about time Trent had a proper chance?"

"Well, there must be a reason he's not getting ice time, Jay," said Wendell. "Judging by what I remember, it's probably coaches thinking he's too small."

Jeez, this old line about Trent's size, I thought. *As if we hadn't heard that enough!* "Wendell, listen to me. That's what everyone has been saying since we first started five seasons ago—Trent's too small, he's going to get hurt out there, and this other garbage that never had any basis in reality. Well guess what? Trent hasn't been hurt yet. In fact, everyone who has ever given him a chance and watched him play said the same thing—no one can hit this kid! He's too quick, and his awareness of the ice is on a completely different level—it's like he's got eyes in the back of his head. I know that looking at the stat sheet, given his size, you might think otherwise, but ask any of his ECHL coaches, this kid's talents are unreal."

"I don't doubt that Trent's talented," said Wendell, "but to be perfectly frank, he's not the type of player that we typically invest in. If I remember correctly, Trent didn't even play hockey for a NCAA Division I team. We don't sign guys unless there's an obvious chance that we may get a return on our investment, and sorry to say, but that return doesn't happen unless they're recognized by someone at the big-time level—the National Hockey League, that is."

"An obvious return on your investment?" I said, getting frustrated. "Gosh darn it, Wendell, if you're so worried about losing money on Trent, then let's take the money out of the equation. I'll tell you what, I'll bring you fifty thousand dollars cash in a briefcase, and if Trent doesn't produce in the first year, I'll eat the cash. What do you think of that, buddy? Tell me, Wendell, what agent do you know who is willing to put their money where their mouth is like I'm offering to do right now?"

"Gosh darn it, Jay. I don't know any agent that would do that, but I'm beginning to think you're out of your mind," Wendell said, hanging up the phone. And that was the last time I spoke to him.

No matter what I said, and no matter how many times Trent proved his value on the ECHL level, it didn't seem to matter. No one was willing to give him a fair shot in the AHL. So things stayed as they were, and Trent got ready for his second season with the Colorado Eagles.

Chapter Forty-Four

Trent stepped right into the captain's role at the start of that season. He was an excellent team leader. With the experience he had—four full seasons in the ECHL—younger players looked up to him, and as it turned out, he was a natural leader and a huge inspiration for guys just coming into the league.

Trent set out on a torrid pace, averaging over one point a game. The Eagles were having a better than average season—well on their way to making another playoff run. I was working the phones constantly, trying to get Trent another chance in the AHL. That chance finally came when I got connected with David Oliver, the GM of the Lake Erie Monsters, an AHL affiliate of the Colorado Avalanche. Sometime in December I was at home watching the game online. When the phone rang, it was late in the third period and the Eagles were out in front by a couple of goals. Trent had already scored twice in the game, so I turned off the computer to talk to Oliver.

"Jay, we'd like to bring Trent up to Lake Erie later this week. Our scouts out in Colorado are telling us it's time to give Trent a good look," said Oliver.

"You'd better believe it's time, David. Sounds great. When do you need him there?"

"As soon as possible—Friday at the latest."

"You've got it! Let me give Trent a call and tell him to get ready," I said and hung up the phone.

It was Tuesday night, so that meant Trent would have to make arrangements to fly out of Loveland as soon as possible. I checked the score in the game and it had ended while I was on the phone, so that meant Trent would be available to talk.

"Trent, great news!" I said when he picked up the phone. "David Oliver from the Lake Erie Monsters called me a few minutes ago, and he wants you over in Cleveland for their game Friday."

"Oh, you've got to be kidding me!"

"I ain't kidding you. I just got off the phone with him—he said their scouts have been watching you."

"Jay, that's amazing, but . . ."

"Heck yeah, it's awesome," I said, interrupting Trent. "This could be a really big shot. So I'll call the airline and arrange a flight. How soon could you fly out? Tomorrow would probably be best; that way you could get settled in and—"

"Jay, listen," Trent said, stopping me in my tracks. "I'd love to go out to Cleveland—I'd fly out right away, in fact—but I can't."

"What? Can't? What are you talking about?"

"Man, I just got a concussion. I was slewfooted, went down hard, and now they're saying I'm out for at least ten days."

"What? No you didn't," I said in utter disbelief. "I was watching the game, you scored two points, and the Eagles were about to win when David Oliver called, and—"

"And thirty seconds before the final buzzer I got a concussion."

"Oh, doesn't that just figure. Of all the gosh darn times to keep you on the ice at the end of a winning game. What the heck's wrong with that Chris Stewart, I swear, sometimes . . ." I was furious. I didn't even want to hear anything else about the ordeal. "Listen, Trent. Don't worry. Get healthy, and I'll do my best to keep David Oliver on the hook. I'll talk to you soon," I said and hung up the phone.

I called David Oliver back and gave him the news, and he was none too happy.

"Jay, you say Trent's got a concussion. Fine, he's not coming to play with us. But I'm not sure I believe you," said David.

"What do you mean you don't believe me? Why would I lie about a thing like that? I may be nuts, but I ain't crazy enough to obstruct Trent from going to the AHL!"

"Well maybe you're not lying, but it feels like someone is. Probably that coach over there in Colorado—trying to keep Trent on his own team."

"Well, I kinda doubt that, David. I just talked to Trent myself and he sounded pretty woozy."

"Okay, Jay. Tough break, I guess."

I asked him if they could wait another ten days, but he said they needed a forward as soon as possible and couldn't wait. I told him not to forget about Trent, that'd he'd be ready when someone else went down for their team, and I hung up the phone completely dismayed. That was another disappointing turn of events, but we didn't let it keep us down. I kept my eye on getting another step closer to the NHL, and Trent got back on the ice ten days later. He was having a great season, despite the concussion, and then about two thirds through the season, I got another call from David Oliver. He wanted to bring Trent up again.

When I got word that Trent was getting a call up to Lake Erie, I felt the need to do something to make sure he wouldn't be put on their fourth line again, so I gave Oliver another call.

"David, this is Jay Storm, Trent Daavettila's agent."

"Hey Jay, great to hear from you. We're super excited to have Trent come over to Cleveland for the three games coming up," said David.

"Yeah, Trent and I are excited too, David. I'm glad you recognized Trent's talent and that you're going to give him a shot on the Monsters' roster. But here's the thing, David. If you're going to call him up and put him on the fourth line, you're just going to be wasting everybody's time. Trent is not a third or fourth liner. He's a first or second liner in the AHL, and he's a first or second liner in the NHL, too, if he could just get the chance. And let me tell you, it's a darn shame that nobody's recognized this fact yet. Every time Trent gets called up to the AHL, the coach puts him on the third or fourth line with a couple of bruisers who can't play, but the reason Trent's been one of the top scorers in the ECHL each of the past four years is because his coaches have played him as the first line center, with other forwards that can play at his level."

"All right, Jay, I understand your frustration. This sort of thing happens with a lot of excellent players at the ECHL level, and I always think it's a shame. So I'll tell you what I'm going to do. The

Monsters are currently fighting for a playoff spot, so I'll bring Trent up and put him on as the second line center until we're statistically eliminated from the postseason. The deal is, Jay, we have to play our draft picks and college free agents as much as possible as soon as we get eliminated from playoff contention, because we want to get the guys we've made an investment in as much time on the ice as possible. But until then, I agree with you that Trent could give us a better chance of winning, so I'm willing to give him a good look on the second line."

What David Oliver had just told me revealed a great deal about what had been holding Trent back this entire time. The NHL clubs had invested draft picks and money in free agents, so they would favor these players over Trent, even if Trent was playing better and gave the team a better chance of winning. It wasn't ever about Trent's talent. No matter how well he played the game, guys in the front offices would be watching the bottom line while Trent was on the front line scoring goals. It was the sad truth of where we were at that point—no matter how many frustrated calls I would make, we couldn't turn back time and get Trent on some Division I college team with a path straight to the draft.

Before I hung up the phone with David Oliver, I said, "Listen, David, put Trent on the second line, and you'll see he's an NHL-caliber player who's been overlooked nearly all his life. He's been a hero for the K-Wings and then a hero for the Eagles, and he could be a hero for the Lake Erie Monsters, too. Let the pond rocket fly, and you'll see what I mean. I'll talk to you after these three games are done."

Trent met the Monsters during a road trip in Charlotte, North Carolina. They had a two-game stand in Charlotte, and Trent didn't waste any time making his presence felt on the ice. During the second game he scored a goal and an assist, and by the end of his three-game stint he had three points total—and a one point per game average is certainly better than most of the darn league. Meanwhile, while Trent was with the Monsters, the Eagles lost three games in his absence. Once again, I was proven right, that when put on a line with good players, Trent would come through big time for his team.

I called up David Oliver, expecting to capitalize on Trent's success with the Monsters.

"So David, what did you think of Trent's performance? Three points over three games is not bad for a second line center who just hopped on your team for the first time last week, is it?"

"You're right, Jay. It's not bad. In fact, it's exceptionally good," said David.

"That's good to hear, David. I'm glad people are starting to recognize that he's an AHL-caliber player," I said.

"Jay, there's no doubt in my mind that this kid could play in the American Hockey League."

"That's right! That's what we've been waiting to hear for all these years."

"The problem, however, is his age."

"Oh, come on, David. His age? He's in tip-top shape at the moment—in the prime of his career!"

"I know it, Jay. I can see that. But it's not the entire picture. You see, we have a bunch of young players straight out of college or juniors who we've already invested money in. We like to get these guys in early and begin training them so they don't develop any bad habits."

"Bad habits? What kind of bad habits does Trent have?"

"Well, none that I can see. Trent seems to have developed really good habits all on his own—phenomenal habits, in fact—but currently we're only looking at draft picks, and although I can see everything you're saying because I saw Trent play for three games, the fact is we have to protect our investment in the younger players first."

"Listen, David, this is what you tell upper management . . ." And I went in to the story about the Maserati that's been parked in the garage, about how it's still like a new car if no one has driven it in fifteen years.

"I hear you, Jay. But unfortunately, that's not how hockey works."

"Well, that's a darn shame, David. If this was baseball and I found a thirty-year-old pitcher who could throw a 101-mile fastball down the strike zone playing sandlot baseball, the Detroit Tigers would come and sign him in a second."

"I hear you, and you're probably right about that. But Jay, hockey is not baseball."

"Well, then hockey is screwed up! Think about it, David, this is a great story for hockey—the kid gets overlooked in college because he's too small, then gets recognized nearly ten years later and becomes one of the top scorers in the league. Newspapers love that kind of stuff. Everybody would be calling you a genius for being the one to call Trent up."

"But I'm telling you, Jay, as soon as upper management sees his age on the stat sheet, they're moving on to the next guy."

"Gosh darn it, who cares about his age? Let the pond rocket run!"

"Believe me, Jay, if there's anyone that's pulling for him, it's me. I know he can play, but I'm just telling you how the business side of it works—we're going with younger guys. But I'll do whatever I can for Trent. If he ever needs a reference, I'll go to bat for him any day of the week to let people know this kid's an American Hockey League–caliber player—at least an American Hockey League caliber player, if not the National Hockey League."

"Okay, David. I appreciate you saying all of that," I said as I hung up the phone.

Chapter Forty-Five

When that second season with the Eagles ended after another playoff, I got a call from Trent.

"Hey Jay, I'm calling because I've got some big news. I want to let you know that I'm coming back to Michigan for the summer. Wendy's pregnant again—she's due in February—and we want to be closer to family while she's pregnant," Trent said.

"Nice! Another kid—congratulations! Where are you guys going to move, exactly? Do you have a place rented out?"

"Actually, no, we don't have a place. Not yet. We are kind of thinking about looking for a place to buy."

"Buy? Well, what about your place in Loveland? Aren't you set up there for next season?"

"That's the thing, Jay." I could tell he was struggling to tell me something. "I've been talking it over with Wendy—three kids now, whew!—and we're sort of thinking about retirement again."

"I see. Sounds like you've got a lot of stuff running through your mind at the moment. Three kids is a huge responsibility," I said, trying my best to be sympathetic even though I hated hearing Trent say the "R" word.

"You're certainly right about my mind racing, Jay. I want to do what's best for my family, but I've got to say my hockey dreams are not dying easily."

"I understand—I hear everything you're saying—three kids, man. Here's what I'd suggest: take your time to think things over. You'll come to the right decision eventually. And when you do, you can bet the Eagles will be waiting for you."

"You're right, Jay, that makes sense. Thanks so much for your support," said Trent.

Although I was trying to keep a positive attitude through this conversation, I wasn't all too happy to hear Trent talk about moving back to Michigan.

After becoming captain of the Eagles the previous season, Trent started to get a lot more attention from local journalists and fans. Every time a story appeared in a newspaper about the Eagles, the writer almost always mentioned team captain Trent Daavettila. This was helpful when I was calling up AHL teams—more and more people in the AHL had already heard about Trent by the time I would get them on the phone, and it was getting easier to get someone to listen to me pitch his playing abilities. One team, the Syracuse Crunch—the Tampa Bay Lightning AHL affiliate—even expressed an interest that seemed sincere, more so than any AHL team had in the past. But with everything going on with Trent, the business end of his career came grinding to a halt that summer.

Then, in what seemed like the nick of time, near the end of the summer, I got a call from Craig Conroy, an assistant general manager with the Adirondack Flames, who were at that time affiliated with the Eagles.

"Jay Storm, this is Craig Conroy with the Adirondack Flames. I'm calling to talk to you about your guy, Trent Daavettila."

"Yes, sir. Good to hear from you. What can I do for you today?"

"Well, Jay, we've had some scouts recommend Trent for a call-up to our training camp this coming fall."

"That sounds good, Craig," I was trying not to show too much excitement to keep him thinking that we had options, to give me some leverage while I tried to get Trent in the best situation possible. "Great! This could be a big deal for a player in Trent's position; it could be his step up into the AHL."

"How about I call you back in a few days after I talk to Trent, and we can go over the details?" I wanted to say yes, but since Trent had mentioned retirement, I took pause.

"Sounds good, Jay," said Craig.

Well gosh darn it, I thought after I hung up the phone. That was the exact kind of phone call that would have shot us over the moon with excitement only a season before. But now I wasn't so sure if telling Trent the news about this camp was going to be the happiest conversation. It didn't matter—I knew I had to stay upbeat and optimistic. He still hadn't said he was definitely retiring, but he also hadn't said he definitely would be playing next season. There was a lot of pressure on this phone call with Trent. The way I saw it, this would be the ultimate test. If Trent was going to play next season, he'd definitely want to take this opportunity to go to the camp, but if he said no, I'd be willing to bet on his retirement come the start of the season. In any case, the only thing to do was to call Trent, tell him about the offer, and see what he had to say.

"Trent! Jay here." I did my best to keep my voice brimming with optimism. "How's everything? How's the family?"

"Everything's good, Jay. Wendy's got a big old baby bump, and Conner's talking. Everybody is healthy."

"That's good to hear."

"Thanks, Jay. So what's going on?" asked Trent.

"Well, I've got some news. I just got off the phone with Craig Conroy, the assistant general manager of the Adirondack Flames. And, well, they want you to go out to Glen Falls, New York, for a training camp in the fall."

"Wow, Jay. Jeez, they just called you out of the blue?"

"Yeah, Craig said that the Flame's scouts had recommended you for a call-up based on your play with the Eagles last season."

"Darn, that certainly is nice to hear, Jay." Trent sounded a bit hesitant.

"Well, like always, you definitely deserve it. You're an AHL-caliber player, if not an NHL one."

"Yeah, Jay. I know you think that."

"Yeah, I know. I haven't forgotten that you're thinking about retirement, but I thought you'd at least like to hear about the offer. I mean, it's up to you to take it, obviously, but I thought you should know what they're offering in any case."

"Yeah, this puts me in kind of a tough spot, Jay."

"Oh, why's that?"

"Well, to tell you the truth, Jay, I've been thinking about hockey all the time—probably even more so when I wasn't considering retirement. I mean, in all honesty, I'd like a shot in the AHL just about more than anything—aside from keeping my family happy and safe."

"Okay, that all sounds smart and good to me. You've got yourself a shot with the AHL come fall," I said, trying to encourage Trent to take up the offer. "But I trust that you'll make the best decision yourself."

"Yeah, I hear you. I'm going to have to talk this over with Wendy. I want to play, but I've got responsibilities—I mean, we're about to have another baby."

"Okay, Trent. I think that Craig is going to need to know pretty soon. So go ahead and talk things over, but try to get back to me as soon as you can."

"I'll do that. Thanks a lot for giving me the news in any case."

After hanging up the phone with Trent, it still wasn't any more clear to me whether or not he'd be retiring before the next season began. I mean, to me it seemed like a no-brainer—this was exactly the kind of break that we'd been looking for. The Adirondack Flames would have scouts all over them from the Calgary Flames, and if Trent were to play a full season there, he surely would be getting some attention from NHL front offices. All of Trent's hockey-playing dreams could come true in that next season if he did well at this camp.

In any case, I could do nothing about Trent's decision of whether or not to go to this camp. It was a shame he had missed the camp the year before with the St. John's IceCaps, and it would be a shame if he missed the camp with the Flames, but these were the breaks with pro hockey in the minor leagues as we had come to know them.

Trent's contemplating retirement didn't stop me from trying to get a new deal, though. If anything, the offer from the Flames had inspired me to keep calling AHL teams. The way I figured it, if the right team in the right town offered Trent a deal, then he'd be more than happy to start off on the AHL level in a new town. So while we waited for Trent to make his decision, I kept calling AHL teams all over the country. Around that time we started to draw interest from one AHL team in particular—the Syracuse Crunch, who were an affiliate of the Tampa Bay Lightning.

A week after the training camp offer came from the Adirondack Flames, I got a call from Trent.

"Well, Jay, I talked it over with Wendy, and we've made a decision about what to do next season." He sounded quite serious, which made me nervous that he was going to say he was going to retire.

"OK," I said. "Whatever you've decided to do, I'm sure it's the best thing."

"Jay, I want to play another year. Although I'm not one hundred percent sold on the idea of going to play an entire season in Glen Falls, I don't want to pass up another AHL camp." Trent sounded more confident and mature than ever. I could tell he had given this decision some serious thought.

"Trent, that is fantastic news!"

"I thought you'd think so, Jay."

"Well, to tell you the truth, I was a little worried about you using that dirty 'R' word again—*retirement*! But I think you made the right decision. You've got this training camp in Glen Falls coming up, and really, there's no ceiling on where that could take you."

"I know, Jay. Like I told you awhile back, I really don't want to retire yet. I love playing hockey more than anything else, and the prospects of doing it at a higher level is too enticing. And I feel blessed that Wendy is willing to tolerate it for another season."

"That's fantastic. Wendy and your kids won't be disappointed."

"I sure hope not. Jay, I've got to say, though, I'm really counting on this being my year. If something doesn't happen soon in regards to moving up a little closer to the NHL, I'm not sure how much longer an ECHL career can sustain me."

"I hear you. So what's your next move then?"

"Well, I'll guess we'll stop thinking about buying a house in Michigan—at least for the moment. And then I better give Chris Ramberg a call so I can get ready for this camp in September."

"That's what I like to hear, Trent! Let's keep our eye on that prize, baby. The NHL is still only a few steps away!"

Chapter Forty-Six

Trent went out to Glen Falls for the training camp in September. He went hard for ten days straight, and afterward everybody was pretty upbeat about him playing out there during the upcoming season. They didn't offer him a contract straight-out, but instead the coaches told him that he should go back to Colorado and play with the Eagles until the Flames were ready to have him join the team in Glen Falls.

So Trent, with family in tow, moved back to their old place in Loveland. To be honest, this is what I think Wendy and the kids wanted to do anyway. They all liked their place in Loveland, and Trent was set to start the next season with his reputation as the team captain cemented firmly in place.

Things didn't go completely as planned at the start of that third season in Colorado. In fact, the season got off to a particularly lousy start for Trent and the Eagles. I got the call from Trent with the bad news the next day after the Eagles' first preseason game.

"Jay, I've got some not-so-great news," Trent said, sounding more worn down than he usually did after a game.

"You don't sound too good, Trent. What's going on?"

"I had a doozie of a first preseason game, Jay. And I can't walk today."

"Well, what's going on? You tired from that camp with Adirondack? I heard you did pretty good out there, and the Flames are thinking about calling you up, you know."

"I know, or at least that's what they told me. But that's not why I can't walk today, Jay. I got hurt yesterday."

"Hurt? What happened?"

"I overextended my knee when trying to deke away from a defensemen, and I just went into the hospital for X-rays and all that."

"So what'd the doctor say, bud?" I was getting pretty worried at this point in the conversation. Trent had never had a bad injury before—aside from that concussion two seasons prior. He'd only missed two games the entire time he'd been playing in the ECHL. And now with the Adirondack Flames knocking on our door, it was a terrible time to be looking at some downtime due to injury.

"It's not good, Jay. It could be worse, but it's definitely not a good thing to be happening right now."

"Well, what is it? Are you going to miss the rest of preseason or something?"

"They're saying it's an MCL tear—not a super serious one, only a second-degree tear—but I'm out up to eight weeks."

"Eight weeks! Well crap, Trent. That doesn't sound right. I've never known you to miss a game."

"I know, Jay, but they say everyone who plays hockey long enough will go down with an injury eventually. To tell you the truth, I feel lucky I've gone as long as I have without missing any significant time to an injury thus far."

"Yeah, I see what you mean. That's a shame. But you've got to keep your chin up. Eight weeks is eight weeks. And I imagine that if you take care of yourself, you might be back even sooner."

"That's true; the doctor did say there's a chance it could heal faster," Trent said, sounding a bit more cheerful.

"So take some time, enjoy a few weeks with your family and watching the games online. Do your exercises, and get ready to come out of the gates running so you can make up for lost time."

"Thanks, Jay. That seems like the right attitude. And you're right, I'm sure Wendy won't mind me hanging out around the house a bit more in the coming months." Then he added, "But Jay, what about the Flames? Have you heard from them at all?"

"Yeah, of course I have! They really like you. Take your time to heal, and then we'll worry about getting you a look at the AHL level when you're better."

"Thanks again. I knew talking to you would cheer me up," Trent said.

Well, I didn't want to say it on the phone to Trent, but that was a heck of a way to start off the season. And right when the Flames were getting ready to call him up to the AHL, too.

And then, wouldn't you know it, about two weeks after Trent's injury, a couple of guys in Adirondack got hurt, and we got a call from their administration inviting Trent to go play with them. That was a tough conversation—telling Craig Conroy that Trent couldn't join the Flames because he was injured. I tried convincing him that he should wait a couple weeks, but Conroy said they couldn't wait. "That's not how the AHL works," he said. Doesn't that just about figure?—chalk up another tally mark in the tough-breaks category for Trent's goal of making it to the NHL. I didn't even tell Trent we got the offer then. I just hoped something else would come along after he got back on the ice.

Chapter Forty-Seven

Trent got back out on the ice early in December of that year, and he jumped right back into what was at that point his typical scoring pace. Despite missing the first two months of the season, he was one of the league's scoring leaders, averaging over a point per game. In fact, he had as many assists in that season, sixty-nine, as he had the previous season, even though he played thirteen fewer games.

The baby—another little girl—came in February, and everybody was happy and healthy. Trent was taking a short paternity leave about the time we got another call from David Oliver of the Lake Erie Monsters.

"Jay, David Oliver here. We've got our eye on your guy, Trent Daavettila, again."

"All right, David. That doesn't surprise me. So what can we do for you?"

"We'd like to bring Trent back to Lake Erie in the next couple weeks. We've got some guys that went down with injuries, and we need to bring in another good forward."

"Okay, David. Now you want to bring in a good forward—and Trent's a good forward." I was trying to get some bargaining leverage, see if I could maybe get Trent into a position to play the rest of the season in the AHL. "He's actually the best forward they've got in Colorado, and he's having a fantastic season, averaging over a point a game."

"I noticed, Jay. I'm actually looking at his stat sheet for the year as we speak."

"So here's the thing, David. If you're going to bring Trent up and out of Colorado to Lake Erie, I'd like to see you do so in a way that would allow him to get some serious playing time on the first or second line. And for more than just two or three games while you wait for someone to come back from a concussion," I said, trying to sound as confident and serious as possible.

"So?" said David, sounding a little irritated.

"So what do you have to say to that?"

"Well, I can't guarantee you guys everything you're looking for, but I'll see what I can do. It so happens we may have a spot on the roster for Trent for the rest of the season."

"That sounds more like it. I'll call Trent and see what he says."

It wasn't easy driving such a hard bargain with David Oliver. After all, he was already offering us something we wanted badly, even if Trent didn't get to play the rest of the season with the Monsters on the first line. In pushing too hard, I risked that he might back off. But I also knew at this point I'd have to be honest with what we really wanted and remain persistent in doing so. I couldn't be afraid of David Oliver saying no or backing out, so I pushed forward, and what do you know? I nudged him a bit in the right direction.

The way things stood, talking David Oliver into possibly letting Trent stay on with the Monsters for the rest of the season was only half the battle. The next step was to call Trent and see how he felt about leaving his family in Colorado and going up to Lake Erie for the rest of the season.

"Trent, you're not going to believe it!" With Trent I made sure to stay optimistic and enthusiastic. I knew we both were going to essentially want the same thing, but what Wendy and the kids thought was a bit unknown.

"Jay, how the heck are you? What's going on?"

"Everything is fantastic up here in Michigan. I assume you're doing well, judging by the number of assists you've made this season."

"That's right," said Trent, laughing a bit. "We're doing real well, Jay."

"That's good. Listen, Trent. I just got a call from David Oliver of the Lake Erie Monsters, and they want you to go back up there as soon as next week."

"Is that so?"

"Yes, sir. I just got off the phone with him. And Trent, he said that he might have a spot for you on the roster for the rest of the season. So this could be a bigger deal than we've seen so far."

"Well, Jay. That sounds pretty darn good."

"And they might be looking to have you start on first or second line."

"Well, that's certainly the best news we've heard from an AHL team."

I could tell Trent was hesitant. As good as the possibility of playing in Lake Erie for the rest of the season may have sounded, clearly something was holding him back—he wasn't his usual enthusiastic self.

"So, what do you think?" I said.

"I think it sounds pretty good."

"Well, all right!"

"But . . ."

"But?"

"Well, Jay, we have a brand new infant in the house."

"I know. Your kids love watching you play hockey."

"But here's the thing, Jay. I'm not sure it's the best time for me to be taking off. I mean, Wendy gave birth only a week ago. I can't just leave her in Loveland to take care of the kids alone—and possibly the rest of the season. To be honest, I don't even know if we could keep our house here if I were to take an opportunity in Lake Erie."

"Okay, Trent. You want to take some time and talk it over with Wendy?" I was getting the picture now that the timing for this deal was completely wrong—Trent leaving a week after his wife gave birth just wasn't the way to start off a stint in the AHL, no matter how you looked at it.

"I will discuss it with Wendy. But Jay, I'm telling you, there's no way I can see leaving right now—not at least for three weeks. Somebody's got to stay here to help take care of the kids, and I don't know anybody but me who could ever do that."

"I hear you, Trent. Listen, this is what I'll tell the Monsters—I'll tell them you can't go because your wife just gave birth and you're going to need some time with the newborn. But in a few weeks, when everyone is settled in, in regards to your family, you'll be ready to head over for the rest of the season. How's that sound?"

"Well, unfortunately, that sounds like the best option we've got at the moment. I hope they still have a spot for me in a few weeks, but we'll see, I guess!"

"Don't worry about it. Take care of yourself. I'll be in touch soon enough," I said.

Two weeks after that, Trent had returned to the ice, playing with the Eagles, so I called him up to see if things were settled in with the newborn enough so that I could give David Oliver a call again and try to get Trent up to Lake Erie for the remainder of the season.

Trent was pumped up on the idea of joining the Monsters, so I called David Oliver. But just our luck, David told me they had filled out their roster with a few other ECHL guys when Trent had turned down the offer a few weeks prior, and then the other players had returned from injuries, so the Monsters no longer had a spot for Trent.

I got pretty darn mad with David Oliver, but no matter what I said to try to persuade him, he wouldn't budge. A missed opportunity was a missed opportunity—you don't get do-overs in professionally hockey, as we had come to learn through all the trials, tribulations, and near misses we had been through.

Chapter Forty-Eight

That third season in Colorado ended with another appearance in the Kelly Cup playoffs. After the Eagles' season ended in the first round of playoffs, Trent and his family decided to stay in Loveland to stick it out for one more season with the Eagles. Meanwhile, I was thinking NHL. My goal was now dead set on getting Trent an appearance in an NHL game. At that point in his career, I thought we were done trying to work our way up through the minor leagues. If Trent could get one shot with an NHL team and score some points, he would prove his worth playing at any level of pro hockey. And the thing is, I knew if he had the right chance on the NHL level, he was just about guaranteed to score some points. That's just the way Trent was—given the chance, he could flourish in any environment.

On the other side of this equation, Trent was clearly going to find his way to a different career outside of professional hockey if something didn't happen in the way of a bigger contract soon. He had brought up retirement the previous two summers, and now with three kids, it would only make sense to think about retirement again this summer, even though he had committed to one more season with the Eagles. The way I figured it, nothing was guaranteed after the upcoming season, so I needed to do my part and try to land at least an AHL contract, and fast.

I called every team in the AHL again, and finally got the ear of Julien BriseBois, the assistant general manager for the Tampa Bay Lightning of the NHL, and the general manager for the Syracuse Crunch of the AHL. I had spoken with Julien a few times in previous seasons about Trent. He knew Trent was deserving of an AHL opportunity and was also impressed with his production on the ice. Julien thought Trent was a tremendous two-way player with great leadership qualities and high character.

Trent's fourth season with the Eagles began without a hitch. And despite the feeling that retirement was looming around the corner, Trent's level of play did not drop off one bit. Once again, he was one of the top scorers in the ECHL, averaging over a point per game. He wound up with eighty total points that year—twenty-five goals and fifty-five assists—a total that matched his top scoring year with the K-Wings five years earlier.

The season was relatively uneventful—there was some chatter about stints with the Lake Erie Monsters again, but no deal appeared that would satisfy the needs of Trent and his family, so he stuck it out in Colorado that entire season. The Eagles won the Western Division and were once again back in the playoffs. That's when I got the phone call from Trent that I had been expecting since the previous summer—the call about retirement.

"Jay, so I've been thinking pretty hard about some stuff—my future and my family and all. And although there's nothing I'd rather do than play pro hockey, I think that, unless something big happens in the coming months, I'm going to hang up my skates and get a steady engineering job."

"Yep, can't say I'm surprised to hear that." I was disappointed, but I had been expecting this call for a long time. "But let me ask you, Trent, what's this 'something big' you mentioned? What do you have in mind exactly?"

"Well, you know. I don't have anything specific in mind. It's just kind of the same dream that's been dangling out there in front of us all these years. I still hope it comes true, but I'm telling you I'm feeling a lot of pressure to move in a different direction right quick, unless something major happens in the way of a step forward."

"You mean like an AHL contract?"

"Yes, absolutely that's what I mean. If all of a sudden you came out with an AHL contract that guaranteed me at least one season with a team—hopefully a team in a decent town that my family would like—then, yeah, I couldn't say no to that."

"Well, if that's what you need, then I'm going to do my best to get that for you."

"I know you are, Jay. But listen, time's running short. So I want to be up front with you—if a good contract doesn't come up by this July, then I'm going back to Michigan to commit to an engineering job."

"This July—okay, that gives me a little time to work. I've got some managers who have been nibbling. I've got no guarantees at the moment, but July is a deadline I can respect."

"Thanks for understanding. I'll keep my fingers crossed for us getting lucky with a contract, but I'm also going to see what I can do about a job back in Michigan."

"Sounds good, Trent. You take care of yourself, and let me see what I can do."

Well, there it was. It was already April, and now I had just three months to land the contract we had been trying to land since we first started out eight years ago by calling up Kenny Holland and the Detroit Red Wings. I didn't have any reason to think that I was any closer now than at any other point in Trent's career, but I'll be darned if anyone thought I was about to give up.

Meanwhile, the Eagles finished out their season by getting knocked out in the first round of the playoffs. They always had an excellent regular season but then fell short in the playoffs.

Chapter Forty-Nine

As that season ended, I started to feel the pressure of the deadline to find Trent an AHL contract. I once again made all the phone calls I could possibly make. By this time I knew I could get the attention of someone in every single professional hockey organization in the Western Hemisphere, because there was always at least one person from each club that would know the name Trent Daavettila. Many of the numbers I was calling I had dialed several times before in the past, and many of them I had been hearing the same thing when someone picked up the phone year in and year out: "Thanks, but no thanks. We know Trent's a good player, but at this point we're not looking to do anything with him."

However, as I said earlier, one guy had been expressing interest in Trent for the past year or so. The best chance we seemed to have for anything like the kind of contract Trent was asking for was with Julien BriseBois and the Tampa Bay Lightning organization. BriseBois was a relatively young hotshot general manager of Canadian origin. He was well respected around the league for being the architect of a championship AHL team—the Syracuse Crunch—and ushering in some Stanley Cup–quality talent through the Lightning's farm system. On top of that, the K-Wings were at the time affiliated with the Tampa Bay Lightning, so it made sense that BriseBois would have heard a few things about Trent through Nick Bootland and the rest of the K-Wings organization, which might have helped explain the high interest in Trent.

Just in the nick of time, around the beginning of May, I got a call back from Julien. "Jay, listen," he said, "we're very interested in signing Trent. But I've got a contract offer out to a guy named Mike Halmo that I'm waiting on at the moment. The thing is, if Halmo doesn't sign this contract within the next two days, I'm going to give the contract to Trent."

"That's frickin' awesome. What do you think the chances are of Halmo signing?"

"I can't say for sure. At the moment his agent's kind of playing hardball, so I'm going to call his bluff and sign Trent if he doesn't get on it soon."

"Why not just sign Trent right now?" I said, a little peeved that he was even considering this Halmo guy over Trent.

"Jay, I know, believe me, my gut is telling me to sign Trent, but right now my head is telling me to sign Halmo—he had twenty-two goals in the American Hockey League last year."

"Yeah, but Julien, your guy Halmo only had like, what, twelve assists?" I said, looking at his stat sheet online. "He only averages half a point a game. Trent's a point-a-game player in the AHL—or any league for that matter. He may only score twenty to thirty goals a season, but he'll have fifty or sixty assists to go with it, instead of the dozen or so that Halmo has got. I'm not trying to throw Halmo under the bus, but I'm just telling you, the guy is just not in the same league as Trent."

"You might be right, Jay, but the thing is, I already have the contract offer out to Halmo, so all we can do now is wait. Don't give up, though, Jay. There's a chance this could work out for you and Trent, so stand by."

"All right, Julien. Thanks for your call. Let us know as soon as you can."

I was on vacation up in northern Michigan while this whole deal with Julien BriseBois, Mike Halmo, and the Tampa Bay Lightning sorted itself out. There was nothing I could do at that point besides wait for the call. BriseBois was the nearest thing we had to an AHL contract, and nobody else was even giving us the time of day anymore. So I decided to do a little fishing, all the while praying and hoping that this Halmo guy would turn down the offer.

I was relaxing by the lake when I got the call from Julien.

"Jay, I've got some bad news for you. It turns out Halmo is going to sign the contract. Sorry to let you down," he informed me.

"Oh, come on, man. You've got to be kidding me! I've been praying and hoping that you guys would come through for us. You're truly the last chance Trent has got." I was heartbroken. All I could think of was Trent's hockey skates hanging in the garage while he started the next season at a brand new engineering job instead of on the ice.

"I know, Jay. To tell the truth, I'm a little disappointed myself. I have to agree with you that Trent does seem like the type of player that belongs in at least the AHL, if not the NHL. Why don't you tell him to go to Kalamazoo for the season, and then we'd likely call him up at some point over the course of the year."

"I hear you on that tip, Julien, but the thing is, Trent's married with three kids now. He's thinking about his family. He's got a bachelor's degree in structural engineering, you know, and he's told me that he's going to be pursuing that path if we can't get him an AHL contract within the next month. He's just taken a job, and the family is all moved back to Michigan from Colorado. I don't see being able to convince him to play another year with the K-Wings."

"Okay, sorry to hear it didn't work out with us. But listen, stay in touch. If you ever have any more players that you want me to look at, don't hesitate to call."

Julien was nice and all, but it didn't matter. We didn't get the contract, and I was certain that Trent was going to retire as soon as I told him the news. I was super bummed out, but at least I could feel confident I had done everything in my power to get Trent as far along as possible. We'd run out of time, and now it seemed like all signs were pointing to Trent moving on to the next stage of his life.

I called up Trent to give him the news.

"Hey listen, Trent," I said. "I hate to say this, but I think it's over. Julien BriseBois and the Lightning ended up signing that Mike Halmo guy, so we're out of luck. They're not going to offer us a contract."

"Hey, Jay, I'm completely fine with that outcome."

"I hear you, but we were so close!"

"Jay, don't worry about it at all. Not for my sake, anyway. I'm real proud of everything we did. It's been an unbelievable journey. I can't thank you enough. I'm completely content with the way things stand right now—moving back to Michigan and getting a good engineering job. I'm just happy I gave it everything I got. We both know that I wanted to make it to the NHL, but those are the breaks, man. Most guys don't even get half as far as I did. We didn't make it, but we went down swinging."

"I hear you. You always did have a heck of a good attitude through all of this, and it's no different through this particular struggle."

"Hey, Jay?"

"What's that, Trent?"

"I quit before you did. And I appreciate that, you know?" I was honestly getting pretty choked up right about then—this whole deal of retirement was pretty darn emotional. After all, a quest that had lasted eight years was coming to an end.

"Hey, Trent," I said. "I appreciate you saying that. But you're not quitting; you're just retiring. You've got different priorities now. And I've got to say, thank you for everything. The journey was fun as heck, to tell you the truth. I would never have dreamed we'd make it this far when we were starting out. It wasn't quite the storybook ending that we wanted, but hey, it is what it is, and I wouldn't have traded it for anything. You're a true warrior, Trent. And I hope you know how much I appreciate you sticking by me all this time."

"I think I do know," he said.

"You know, Trent, if you played 450 games in your career, I bet I watched 447 of them—and the ones that I missed were likely only due to my wife having a baby on that very day, or else I was in the hospital myself." That's true, too—I had watched nearly every game online if not in person. I'd watch the game, and then I'd call Trent up after and tell him where he looked good and where he had screwed up. And darn it if I wasn't going to miss doing that. Never had I felt so involved with the sport I loved; never had hockey felt so important to me. I certainly was going to be missing all that next season.

Chapter Fifty

After that contract fell through with the Tampa Bay Lightning, Trent secured a good job with an architecture and engineering firm in the metro Detroit area. He and his family packed up their stuff in Colorado and moved it all to a nice place in Trent's hometown of Howell.

If I'm being truthful with myself, despite wishing Trent had played at least one more year, life in Michigan did seem to suit him and his family better than the ECHL player life in Loveland. They were closer to family, the kids could go to the same schools their parents had gone to, and Trent took a lot of pressure off himself now that he was in a steady job that was guaranteed for the foreseeable future.

And then, somewhere near the end of July, something happened that just about near knocked my socks off. Out of the blue I got a call from Julien BriseBois again. "Jay, I'm calling because I've had this nagging feeling all summer about not signing Trent—it's just not sitting right with me. So I want to do something for you guys."

"What's that, Julien?" I said while at the same time thinking, *Oh, jeez, now Julian comes out saying that he regrets signing Trent after the retirement has already been announced, the local newspaper is about to print a story about it, and Trent's already bought a house in Michigan. Some timing, Julien!*

"I'll tell you what. The Tampa Bay management and I have been talking about Trent. I just emailed you a letter, and what that letter said is that we'd like to invite Trent to our NHL training camp coming up this fall."

The bottom just about dropped out of my stomach. "What?" I exclaimed. "You have got to be kidding me. Am I hearing you right? You're inviting Trent to the NHL training camp?" The NHL training camp was a huge deal. Spots in these camps were almost exclusively reserved for players who actually had a good shot to be playing in the NHL that year. The fact that Trent was all of a sudden getting this opportunity was nearly unthinkable.

Julien chuckled a bit and said, "Yep, you heard me right, Jay. We want him to come to our training camp so he can play in front of all our NHL scouts and the NHL management. Trent will finally get a chance to see if he can keep up with players on the NHL level."

"Wow, Julien, that sounds phenomenal. I can't thank you enough for inviting him. And, of course, I wouldn't want anything more for Trent and his playing career." My heart was beating incredibly fast, and my palms were sweating on the phone receiver. I wanted so bad to simply say, "Yes sir, see you at the NHL training camp this fall," but I couldn't say that. It wasn't my call at that point. So instead I said, "But to be honest with you, I've got to talk to Trent first. I hate to say it at this point, but Trent might be done, man." I paused for a second, trying to get a handle on what the heck was going on in this highly unusual moment. "But Julien, you inviting him to the camp just might change his mind about retirement. Trent had given me until

July 1st to get him an AHL deal, but we'll just see if this kind of an opportunity might convince him to keep at it a bit longer."

"Okay, Jay. We want him. We want to take a look at him, at least. So let us know as soon as you do."

I hung up the phone with my head spinning. I ran to the computer to check the email the Julien had sent, and there it was—a document with the Tampa Bay Lightning letterhead. It specified that the training camp was only a month away, they hoped Trent was in good shape, because they had high expectations for that season, and all this other stuff that made it sound like they had been expecting Trent to be attending the training camp this whole time.

I was so excited in that moment that I almost completely forgot about Trent and his retirement. I had tried to stay as optimistic as I possibly could on the phone with Julien in regards to Trent coming out of retirement now with the chance of attending this camp, but the truth is, I wasn't so sure that Trent was going to want to do that. He had seemed pretty content with settling down in Howell and working his new job. Not only had Trent said he was content, but I could see it, too. It all made perfect sense to me that he was happier in a stable place with his wife and three kids. But on the other hand, what person who grew up playing hockey, loving the game about as much as anything in the world, would turn down an opportunity to attend an NHL training camp? This was our dream coming true before our eyes.

Only one thing would be able to make my head stop spinning, and that was to call Trent.

"Trent, you're not going to believe this!" I was so excited, the words practically shot out of my mouth. I could hardly keep up with my own thoughts. "You've just been invited to go to the NHL!"

"What?" he said, sounding shocked.

"Trent, listen to me. I just got off the phone with Julien BriseBois, the assistant general manager of the Tampa Bay Lightning, and general manager Steve Yzerman just emailed me a letter inviting you to their NHL training camp in the fall."

"What?" Trent said again. "Jay, no way! You've got to be kidding me. Where is this even coming from?" Trent sounded like he wondered if I had lost my mind and was fabricating this whole offer.

"Listen to me. It's real. I'm forwarding you the letter right now."

I sent Trent the letter, and I could tell he nearly fell out of his chair when he opened the email.

"Wow, this is unbelievable. What the heck! Is this real?"

"It's real," I said.

"Jay, let me go talk to Wendy. We'll see how it goes over—but Jay, I really don't think I can pass up this opportunity."

"I know, Trent. I was thinking the exact same thing."

I hung up the phone and waited for Trent's reply. He took a whole two days to get back to me, and the entire time while I waited, I got more and more nervous about his answer. I tried to see it both ways—sure, Trent was a father of three now, and he needed to take care of his family above all else. But heck, what if he went to this camp and got an NHL contract with the Tampa Bay Lightning? The average contract for someone in Trent's position certainly would have been much better than an engineering job. Plus he'd be playing the game he had loved his whole life!

On the other hand, what if Trent didn't make the team and missed out on that engineering job he'd just landed near Detroit? I hated to think that Trent wouldn't make the team. I believe strongly in the power of positive thinking—optimism has been one the keys to success in my experience—but I had to try to see it from Trent's perspective, too. This thought must have crossed his mind—coming back from a ten-day camp out in Tampa Bay with no contract, no engineering job, and a family of five waiting for him. Just because I was sure he would land a contract, after all, didn't make it so, as we had seen in the past. What if the Lightning organization told him to go play in Kalamazoo for the season until they were ready to call him up, like BriseBois had suggested? I felt lousy simply recalling that conversation with Julien. I sure as heck knew Trent wouldn't be wanting to play in Kalamazoo next season. He'd probably never forgive me if he went and did the training camp and ended up back with the K-Wings, the same darn place he'd started out in.

I waited for two days with all these thoughts swirling around my head. I even lost a little sleep. Then, on the evening of the second day, Trent called me.

"You know what, Jay?" Trent said. "I talked to my wife, and it just kills me to say this, but I have got to say no to the offer. I can't go to that training camp."

"What? Are you serious. Why, Trent?"

"Jay, it's just time, man," he said. "I turned the page after the first of July. I have a steady job now and started the process of buying a house."

"But you have a shot of getting a job playing hockey in the NHL," I said, feeling confused and sad at the same time, but wishing I could understand what Trent was going through.

"I know, but the thing is, Jay, I stopped training about four weeks ago, and I don't even see how I could get back in shape in time. As much as I want to go to the camp, the last thing I want to do is go to the camp and not come out with a decent contract."

"Jeez, no one told me you had quit training."

"Yeah, you know, Jay, if I hadn't taken those four weeks off, I would be going to that camp without a doubt, but given the fact that I'm out of shape now changes everything. I've got too much respect for you, for myself, and for the Tampa Bay Lightning organization to report there out of shape and try to keep up with NHL players. If I had eighty workouts in and I was confident I was one hundred percent in shape, it would be a different story. But the way things are now, my answer is no, I'm not going to take that opportunity."

"Wow, Trent, I respect what you're saying, but it's near about killing me," I said, trying to hold back my emotions.

"I know, Jay. I know it's killing you, because it's killing me too. I really wish things would have turned out differently earlier."

"Come on now. We both wish things had turned out differently, but we were dealt the cards we were for a reason—no regrets."

"I hear you. I have to say it does feel pretty good to get as far as we have. When all is said and done, I'm still at peace with my career. And I've also got to say, it feels pretty cool to be getting a letter from Steve Yzerman inviting a thirty-two-year-old former ECHL player to an NHL training camp."

"Ha! I certainly agree with you there. It does feel pretty cool to have that letter."

"It's unbelievable! You did some unbelievable work for me. I can't imagine how you even pulled this off—that letter, it's giving me goosebumps—to think I got recognized with enough respect to warrant a tryout with one of the best teams in the NHL. Darn it, that feels pretty good."

"Hey, Trent, never for one second doubt that that letter is the kind of treatment you should have been receiving since you first started out playing in the men's leagues."

"Jay, again, let me say it—I quit before you did. I feel like I'm letting you down."

"Hey, you're not letting me down at all. I'm proud of you, Trent. It's been an unbelievable journey, and getting this letter—knowing that we were right about you being NHL-caliber talent this whole time—is extremely validating. I think I might put that letter in a frame when the hard copy arrives by mail, in fact. Because that letter alone is pretty impressive, if you ask me."

"You know, you're right. I wouldn't mind framing that letter either—to think how close we were this entire time. I never want to forget this feeling for the rest of my life."

"It was our goal when we started out, remember? I said the NHL is our end goal. Well, I guess this is the end, and in a way, we reached our goal."

"I couldn't agree with you more, Jay. It feels about like the perfect ending to this journey, in fact."

Chapter Fifty-One

Well, that's nearly the entire story of Trent Daavettila's hockey career. Sure, I could go into detail about how Julien BriseBois reacted when I called him up to tell him that Trent wouldn't be attending the camp—how he said that it made no sense, that he was completely flabbergasted, that Trent was missing the opportunity of a lifetime, and nearly any kid who had ever laced up a pair of hockey skates would be dying to get a chance like Trent was getting. Or I could go on about how Trent settled into a nice home, and all the newspapers around Loveland and Kalamazoo wrote sad but sweet articles about his retirement. But you can probably imagine yourself how that all went. It may not be the type of happy ending somebody might expect when I first started off telling this story—the one that ends with Trent hoisting up a Stanley Cup at the end of a championship season—but I'd still say it's a happy ending. In any case, you can believe me when I say that Trent is happy, whether it's the ending everybody was expecting or not.

As for me, my insurance business is keeping me plenty busy at the moment. I'm still working the phones as hard as ever. Whether I'm calling to try and get someone a better insurance deal or calling about an usually talented hockey player, my work ethic remains the same.

And, oh yeah, during last season, when I had all this extra time on my hands, considering that I was no longer acting as Trent's agent, I built my boys a nice little hockey rink in the backyard, and some of the kids in the neighborhood have been coming by to skate. And you know, the way a couple of these boys play, it makes me wonder if I'll have another opportunity to try to land a big-time contract for an up-and-coming pond rocket in the near future.